The
DERBYSHIRE
and
NOTTINGHAMSHIRE
WEATHER
BOOK

Len Markham

WITH AN INTRODUCTION
by Charlie Neil

COUNTRYSIDE BOOKS
NEWBURY, BERKSHIRE

COUNTRYSIDE BOOKS
3 Catherine Road
Newbury, Berkshire

ISBN 1 85306 282 0

Front Cover: Queens Drive, Nottingham, March 1947.
(Nottingham Evening Post)

Back Cover: The Midland Arms, Belvedere Street, Mansfield,
January 1976. (Chad-Mansfield Chronicle Advertiser)

Designed by Mon Mohan

Produced through MRM Associates Ltd., Reading
Typeset by Paragon Typesetters, Clwyd
Printed in England

FOREWORD

The first recorded weather notes for these islands can be reliably traced to 30th August 55 BC. First in an illustrious line of commentators and forecasters, Julius Caesar, in his *De Bello Gallico,* described the stormy conditions off the Kent coast 'tanta tempestas...' Weather reports and predictions have been a notable feature of all our daily lives ever since.

The twin counties of Derbyshire and Nottinghamshire have themselves experienced many notable weather extremes over the centuries. Geographically bound and drawn together by a common heritage, together they have a long and a remarkably well documented history of elemental contest with rain, wind and fire.

This book bestrides the two counties. From the shivering Snake Pass to the borders of Lincolnshire, and from the great cities of Derby and Nottingham to the flood plain of the Trent and beyond, we take a broad sweep, spanning the miles and the years to reveal a catalogue of weather extremes. These extraordinary climatological excesses are writ large, typically in the glacier-etched rocks of the High Peak, the corkscrew spire of Chesterfield parish church and in the phoenix-like Trent river bridges – in the meteorological order of things a veritable succession of ninepins long assaulted by floods. Herein are floods and tempests galore, lightning strikes, blizzards, droughts and for good measure occasional earthquakes and tornadoes. Derived from ancient journals, personal diaries, weather station forecasts, scientific analyses, newspaper archives and a host of personal reminiscences, the accounts of these exceptional days will, I hope, make for exciting reading.

A snow cutting in the High Peak at Higger Tor, February 1947.
(Derbyshire Record Office)

A contrary companion, begetter of harvests and grinder of tombstones, weather is a vital cog in the ever transient nature of this globe. And I was reminded of certain dusty words of the funeral service in compiling this book. Hindered by snow and ice, research was a slow process, but I soon discovered that counter to popular belief, even the hallowed documents of our archival services are not immutable. Attached to certain rainfall statistics in the Derby Local Studies Centre, a scribbled note says it all. 'Rainfall charts were once damaged in flood water, in consequence many of them may be illegible in whole or in part.'

Leonard Markham

CONTENTS

'St Agnes' Eve! Ah, bitter chill it was!
The owl, for all his feathers, was a-cold;
The hare limp'd trembling through the frozen grass
And silent was the flock in woolly fold'

Keats

INTRODUCTION

by Charlie Neil

 I feel I ought to start this introduction with an apology to those who live on the high ground of Derbyshire. As a weather presenter for Central Television, the high ground of Derbyshire features heavily: If there's ever any less than good weather ANYWHERE in the region, it always seems to be '.... over the high ground of Derbyshire'! If TV still had those blackboards with a pointed stick for the forecaster to use, I'm sure I'd have worn a hole over The Peaks by now.

I did my first weather presentation for Central TV on 10th January 1991. A memorable day. It was my first job in TV ... and ... my first real dealings with weather. The meteorologists I work with soon got used to me asking dumb questions; like 'what's anticyclonic gloom when it's at home?' ... and ... 'why?' Three and a half years later I'm still asking, but these days the questions are not quite so dumb. And it's testament to the patience and enthusiasm of all the meteorologists at The Weather Department that it's been a very enjoyable three and a half year learning curve. Somewhere along the line I've become as much a fully paid up 'weather anorak' as they are. I do things like drive to the nearest high ground after a gale warning – just to stand there and feel the power of the wind ... or stand outside in the thunderstorms to track the course of the cloud and lightning.

7

This is a woman who years ago, would get up and put the kettle on when the news finished!

The British have a special relationship with the weather. It brings people together... the sense of comradeship when we're all battling through the elements to get to places and the tales of heroism in extreme cases. As a weather presenter, that comradeship is there all the time. People not only assume they know me well because they see me on TV most nights but they assume they know me as well as they know a neighbour or a member of the family. And it's because I'm talking to them about the weather, just like someone popping round for a cup of tea. I've had good natured banter hollered to me from the other end of the supermarket queue on more occasions than I care to remember! Even if a forecast has gone terribly wrong – it doesn't seem to matter to the viewer. 'It's the weather' they say, 'it's got a mind of its own!' There's a serious and lighter side to the weather, and it's that delicate balance which makes my job so interesting. TV weather is generally a 'straight' act, it's a science and isn't therefore expected to get a barrel of laughs but I enjoy treating the subject as a viewer would. If there's a red alert flood warning being issued, you have a responsibility to be serious about it, but if I can get away with adding 'buy a rubber dinghy' on the list of precautions to take, then I will. Just like that friend who's popped round for a cup of tea. I don't know of any other area of science where this could happen, or of any other part of the world where it *does*.

Over the last few years, weather has become BIG! TV weather graphics are bright and exciting... national presenters are household names... and sponsors clamour to put their money where the sunshine is. It's now even a subject on the National Curriculum. But interest in weather is as old as the hills. The wealth of historical extracts in this book just goes to prove it. You'll read here, of the man who made an igloo for his two pigs, complete with all mod cons, during a hard winter down by the

Trent. It sounds like one of those lighter stories at the end of News At Ten, doesn't it? In fact it happened during the 13 week frost in 1814. Even then, in times of great weather extremes that could cause untold misery and sadness, there was the ability to see the humour of the situation. And it's a humour as British as this lovely weather of ours. I bet that pigman would have got on famously with Gary Draper, the shopkeeper shown in the book, selling snow for '50p a box while stocks last'!

Times may change . . . technology may advance . . . but that good old leveller, the British weather, is still catching us out. I thought it was a fairly modern phenomenon to blame the weather forecaster for things like winter, so I was interested to read Len's account of the Big Freeze of 1947. At the end of the freeze, the Secretary of State for Air was grilled in the House of Commons about the lack of warning and planning during the crisis. He came up with a good excuse ' . . . to my regret, I must admit that the science of meteorology still leaves much to be desired (laughter and cheers)'. Things haven't changed much since then have they?

It's not every day that the weather gets to be debated in The Commons but it has always been and will always be, THE great British conversation starter. The interest must stem from the sheer variety of weather we have. Think how boring it must be to have a conversation with a stranger on the equator! The sheer contrasts in topography around Nottinghamshire and Derbyshire, from the Peaks to the valleys, with the resulting dramatic range of weather through the seasons, must make the natives the best conversationalists in our land!

In this Weather Book you will find both affection and humour. And if you want to arm yourself with myriad facts and stories to drop into a conversation, then read on . . .

Charlie Neil
July 1994

9

'What bait yer using luv?' Supplies get through to a house in Bosworth Road in Nottingham's Meadows area, March 1947. (Nottingham Evening Post)

STAR WARS AND THE LITTLE ICE AGE

18th September 1253: Star Wars

An aerial spectacle mesmerised the villagers of Alvaston near Derby as the sun set. The aged lord of the manor, Sir Thomas Hanselin, his son Galfred and a knot of astounded onlookers witnessed the event. 'Suddenly in a wide dark cloud there appeared a large, bright star, like the radiant sun, and near it two small red stars, like sparkling candles, which instantly leaped fiercely towards the great star, and (as we may say) were attacking it, rushing upon it and waging a desperate war with it; so that it seemed to those who were witnesses to this sight that fiery particles descended from them. The combat lasted until the close of evening, so that those who beheld it, ignorant of what it might portend, retired to their homes struck with terror and astonishment.'

1450 – 1850: The Little Ice Age

During a 400 year long period known to meteorologists as the Little Ice Age, Arctic pack ice expanded and northern hemisphere temperatures were much depressed. Between 1407-08 and 1564-65 the river Thames froze six times. During the winter of 1607-08 Queen Elizabeth I regularly strolled on the frozen river

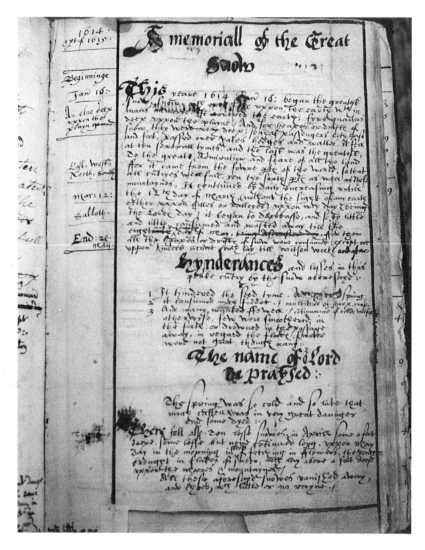

Record of the Great Snow, 1614-1615. (Derbyshire Record Office)

and impromptu football matches were held on the ice. The first Frost Fair took place in 1607-08, an assembly of river top booths and side shows delighting Londoners. Ice skating was, according

12

to legend, first demonstrated to the King on the Thames in 1662-63. The most celebrated Frost Fair was held in 1683-84 when the frozen conditions persisted for two months. The last fair was held in 1814, *The Morning Post* reporting on 3rd February 'An elephant on the ice... Yesterday a very fine elephant crossed the Thames a little below Blackfriars Bridge; the singularity of such an animal on the ice attracted a great concourse...'

In this region, two accounts serve to indicate the severity of the arctic conditions.

1614 – 15: The Great Snow

'This year 1614 began the greatyst snow which ever fell within many memorye. And for heaps or drifts of snow they were very deep; so that passengers both horse and foot, passed over gates and hedges and walls it fell at ten severall times, and the last was the greatest. To the great admiration and feare of all the land, for it came from the four parts of the world so that all countrys from the south part as well as these mountaynes. It continued by daily increasing until 12th day of March without the sight of any earth, either upon hilles or valleyes upon which day (being the Lords Day) it began to decrease, and so by little and little consumed and wasted away till the eight and twentyeth day of May before all the heaps and drifts of snow were consumed: except one upon Kinders Scowt which lay til Witsun Weeke and after.
Hyndrances and losses in this peake country by the snow aforesayd

1 It hindered the seedtime.
2 It consumed much fodder/multitude of sheep-cause.
3 Any many wanted fawell continuance of colde wether otherwyse few were smothered in the full or drowned in the

passage away in regard the floods of water were not great though many.

The name of the Lord be praised.

The Spring was so cold and so late that much Cattel was in very great danger and some dyed. There fell also ten snowes in April some a foot deep some less but none continued long. Upon May Day in the morning in stead of fetching in flowers the Youth brought flakes of snow which lay about a foot deep upon the moores and mountaynes. All the aforesaid snowes vanished away and thord with little or no rayn'.

(Youlgreave Churchwardens and Constables Accounts 1604-1722)

1814: The Thirteen Week Frost

Beginning on Christmas Eve 1813, a strait-jacket frost held Nottingham in its grip for 13 weeks. Record low temperatures were experienced, the thermometer registering a numbing New Year low of – 17°C at Lenton Priory on 14th January. The river Trent and local canals froze solid, and, encased in thick ice, roads became all but impassable.

The novelty of walking on water and opportunities for skating encouraged local people to flock to the Trent. Bonfires were lit along the bankside between Trent Bridge and Wilford Ferry. Meals were cooked on the ice and one wit using the accumulated ice in Market Place even carved himself an icy pig-sty fitted with a door and two prize sows! But chilly entertainments apart, it was an arduous time.

Handbill to commemorate the tremendous tornado of 12th May 1811. (Derbyshire Record Office)

THE WEATHER IN THE
EARLY YEARS

664: Ancient records attest to the earliest reliably known hot summer during Britain's driest ever century.

763-4: Details of the severe winter are the earliest on record.

1110: Nottingham experienced a frightening earthquake – the first to be recorded in England. According to the Canon of Leicester, the river Trent dried up for several hours. 'This river . . . did become dry of a sudden at Nottingham and no question but it was so at other places, which could not have happened had not the springs been supplied by subteranneous passages, which, casually stopped by the fall of earth, could not furnish water . . . '

1255: On 13th July, a hailstorm, 'astonishing beyond measure', struck the valley of the Trent between Wichnor Bridge and the village of Repton. Flailing volleys of hailstones were followed by a whirlwind, 'overwhelming and carrying away the land, with buildings and the corn in the field. The destruction of the hay was universal throughout the vale of the Trent by inundations of the waters, such as had not been known during a long series of years.'

1346: In the Trent valley between midsummer and Christmas, 'long continued rains' caused some of the worst flooding in locally recorded history.

1354: Parched Nottinghamshire suffered a great drought, no rain having fallen from the end of March to the end of July.

1541: A nationwide drought reduced the Trent and other rivers to the state of 'straggling brooks'.

1545: On 20th June, an awe inspiring tornado cut a swathe across Derbyshire, an old chronicle attributing the phenomenon to the Devil, who '. . . went to Wyndley Lane (in Duffield parish) . . . and from thence he went to Belper, and then he hath pullyed and rent upon x1 housses: and from thence he went to Belper Wood and he hath pullyd down a wonderous thyng of wood and kylled many beaste: and from thence to Heage, and these hath he pullyd downe the chappyl and the most part of the towne.' Examination of this account indicates that Old Nick flew from south-west to north-east along a track of at least five miles in length.

1587: Derby Church Swept Away

After torrential rain, the church of St Mary's was demolished by a tide of floodwater. So great was the force of the torrent that the mills in St Michaels Lane were carried away.

1588: Hailstones Like Cannonballs!

In this year of the Armada, not to be outdone by accounts of the atrocious weather conditions at sea, 'Bakers Chronicle' relates the following: 'On the 7th July in this year, within a mile of Nottingham, was a marvellous tempest of thunder, which, as it came through two towns, beat down all the houses and churches. The bells were cast to the outside of the churchyard, and some webs of lead 400 feet into the field, writhen like leather. The river Trent, running between the two towns, the water with the mud at the bottom was carried a quarter of a mile and cast against trees, with the violence whereof the trees were torn up by the roots, and cast 12 score yards off. Also a child was taken forth off a man's hand and carried two spears' length high, and then let fall 200 feet off, of which fall it died. Five or six men thereabouts were slain by the storm, during which hailstones fell measuring 15 inches in circumference.'

1591: 'There was an uncommon drought which was exceedingly injurious to vegetation particularly on the fandy grounds about Nottingham. It being fucceeded this summer by ftrong wefterly winds and little rain, the Trent and other rivers were almost without water.'

THE
SEVENTEENTH CENTURY

1607: A pitiless frost abided for weeks bringing death to many poor families throughout the region. The agonies of the poor were particularly acute in Newark. A contemporary chronicler described their plight . . . 'divers of the poorer sorte weepinge in pittifull manner did earnestly entreate John Franklin (overseer of the mills) that they mighte have their corne to be speedily grounde, els should they be bitterly distressed with famine through want of bread, in that most of the water milnes in the countrie were then frozen.'

1610: Prisoners Drowned In Their Cells

Beginning on Michaelmas Day in the morning, blizzards raged throughout Derbyshire. The ferocity of the snowstorms was unparalleled in recent history. The year was also noted for exceptional rainfall in Derby where the notorious Markeaton Brook again overflowed its banks. So sudden was the spate, that three frantic prisoners in the town gaol were drowned like rats.

Corkscrew spire of Chesterfield parish church, Derbyshire. The twist is attributed to the warping action of the sun on green timber . . . though legend has it that Old Nick alighted on the spire for a rest en route from Nottingham. A waft of incense from below caused him to sneeze so violently that his perch became twisted. (Len Markham)

1615: Tissington's Famous Wells

The former importance of communal wells to the life of Peak District villages is symbolised by annual ceremonies of well dressing – thanksgiving services, some assert, for Nature's unfailing providence. At Tissington, the ceremony could well date back to the great drought of 1615. In that parched year, no rain fell in the neighbourhood (except for one solitary shower of no intensity in May) between 25th March and the 4th August and there was a grave lack of water. Most local wells failed but Tissington's springs kept flowing and there has been an Ascension Day celebration ever since.

1624: Prolonged summer sunshine dessicated the Nottingham-shire countryside, rendering heaths and forests vulnerable to fire. On 23rd August, an ember from a consignment of still hot charcoal accidently fell amongst tinder dry ling and there was an instant conflagration. The blaze spread with great rapidity, consuming a vast area of forest some four miles long and one and a half miles wide. Newark, seven miles from the scene, was covered in thick smoke as hundreds of men tried to contain the fire by digging trenches. Fortunately the wind changed direction at the moment the fire was approaching the northern end of an extensive wood that at that time extended from Mansfield to Nottingham.

November 1655: Freeze Arrests Plague

Brought to the Derbyshire village of Eyam by an unsuspecting journeyman from London, a plague-infected bundle of clothes spread its deadly pestilence throughout September. Six victims were buried by the end of the month, a further 23 fatalities being registered in October. The pestilence was known to thrive in hot and humid conditions and all hope was pinned on the advent of the normally unwelcomed winter and sub zero temperatures which it was thought might end the epidemic. A cold snap helped restrict the death toll in November to seven, but in subsequent months many more inhabitants perished, the final tally being 259 out of a total population of 350.

1601: Weakened by successive floods of the notorious Markeaton Brook, the tower of St Werburgh's church in Derby collapsed in a gale.

1624: '5s 6d Paid to John Fletcher, Edward Battye, Richarde Oker, with others, for breakin the yce after the great frost, to prevent the bridges from danger.' (Extract from Nottingham Borough Bridge Masters' Accounts 1623-24)

1661: The river Derwent in Derby was so dry that its inhabitants crossed its bed dry shod.

1662: A dreadful hurricane in Derby uprooted trees, stripped hundreds of tiles from roofs in Market Place and Full Street and blew away the steeple of St Werburgh's church.

1680: The spire of St Mary's church in Edwinstowe, Nottinghamshire, where Robin Hood is said to have married Maid Marion, was rebuilt after a great storm.

1682-83: A severe and prolonged frost lasting from early September 1682 to 5th February 1683 inflicted much hardship in Derbyshire and Nottinghamshire. Fuel and foodstuffs were in short supply and river traffic on the Trent was brought to a standstill. The bridge in Nottingham was 'broke down' by the weight of ice.

1698: The scourge of the Markeaton Brook again afflicted St Werburgh's church in Derby, much of its fabric being undermined in a cataclysmic flood.

THE EIGHTEENTH CENTURY

11th February 1772: Frozen to Death

Following an intense period of frost, so severe as to congeal lantern oil and render street lamps inoperative, the temperature in Nottinghamshire dropped to an all time low. The night of the 11th February was so intensely cold that several travellers were frozen dead in their tracks. After attending Nottingham market, Ann Webster of Calverton trudged home in appalling blizzard conditions, succumbing together with her horse only one mile from home. Two samaritans on the road to Mansfield suffered a similar fate. Thomas Rhodes and John Curtis were ploughing through the drifts with their team of horses when they came upon a lone pedestrian, a soldier, whose life was in danger. Unhitching the leading mount they bade the soldier ride to Nottingham and proceeded to follow. But the remaining horses, unaccustomed to the loss of the leading nag, obstinately refused to move. Two frozen corpses were found the following morning. There were other fatalities on that fearful night, the horrors being much magnified by the poor state of the roads.

1795: The Candlemas Flood

From Christmas Eve 1794 to 9th February 1795, the two counties endured an appalling winter of remorseless frost and frequent snows. And then at Candlemas came the long-dreaded thaw, the temperatures soaring overnight to release a snowy meltdown that flooded the Trent valley.

Torrents of water from Derbyshire's feeding streams coursed from the hills, water and ice-floes thrashing down the Trent and causing destruction on a vast scale. The outer river bank near Spalford burst, allowing millions of gallons of water to spew forth, converting over 20,000 acres of farmland west of Lincoln into one vast sea. Heroic efforts by an army of workmen using 80 tons of faggots and 400 tons of earth eventually stemmed the flow.

Completely surrounded by water, the inhabitants of Narrow Marsh were imprisoned in their homes for two days, Girton village was submerged to a depth of three ft and the flood threatened the church at North Collingham, rising to a height of four ft six inches on the churchyard wall.

18th Century Weather Notes

1714: A great storm blew trees down in Sherwood Forest to the value of £2,473.

1726: On 24th January a London newspaper gave the following graphic report . . . 'There is an account from Newark of a very great inundation of the River Trent which broke its banks and overflow'd a great tract of the county, so that the mails to and from the North were ferr'd over a water of five miles broad, and they found it very difficult to get boats for that purpose.'

1735: 'The Trent was so vastly swell'd that the quantity of water broke down the bridge.'

1738: On 13th July, a report in a Derby news-sheet, described the effects of an early morning call. Earth tremors were felt in the town and surrounding villages before dawn and abed there was great consternation. Damage to buildings was slight but in nearby Caldwell, a barn belonging to local farmer Samuel Sanders was demolished.

1740: Three Yorkshire clergymen were lost in the snow after attending the funeral of their friend Ralph Rigby, a curate at Eyam church, Derbyshire. Daylight revealed two frozen corpses and one survivor near to death.

On 11th December, after 48 hours of torrential rain interspersed with snow showers, Derby was devastated by a great flood.. Several town centre thoroughfares were inundated and there was widespread flooding of commercial and residential properties. Cattle and sheep were swept away in the deluge, bridges were demolished and St Werburgh's church suffered considerable structural damage.

1750: Dogs howled in 'unearthly tones' and fish jumped 'half a yard' above the Trent during an earthquake.

1764: A tremendous thunderstorm rained down on Nottingham. A number of people were 'stricken to the ground' by lightning, but thankfully none were killed. There was significant damage in Lenton and Wilford.

1770: A tidal wave of water breached the Trent river banks near Newton and Torksey destroying huge quantities of hay and corn.

1772: Plummeting January temperatures caused lighting oil in street lights to congeal. Nottingham streets were blacked out.

1795: An earth tremor, preceded by a noise like thunder, demolished dozens of chimneys and rang church bells in Nottingham.

After 120 hours of continuous rain the Trent rose twelve and a half ft and reached a record high at Trent Bridge, Nottingham of 80.55 ft above mean sea level.

1795: A sudden thaw after seven weeks of continuous frost caused flooding on a massive scale, the rivers Trent and Witham combining in one roaring torrent. Normanton-on-Trent suffered badly.

1797: Arising near Worksop on 23rd July a cyclonic wind raged north-east cutting a swathe of destruction three miles wide. Hay stacks were picked up like gossamer, buildings were thrown down and there was extensive damage to timber in Sherwood Forest. The wind cut a path 30 yards wide through a spruce plantation near Scofton, demolishing every tree except one lone specimen, which unaccountably stood firm in the face of the storm.

THE NINETEENTH CENTURY

2nd August 1801: Sick Beds Swamped

Bingham in Nottinghamshire was visited by a dreadful storm . . . 'the lightning was extremely vivid – the thunder awfully loud and terrific – and the rain, for more than an hour descended in torrents . . .' Two lambs and a horse were struck dead by lightning at Whatton and a barn at nearby Granby was set on fire. Preceded by a barrage of hail – some of the projectiles were of marble size – rain 'did infinite mischief to the cellars and storehouses of several inhabitants who reside in the lower parts of the town, particularly Greyfriars Gate and Fishergate; at the former street, a ball of electric fluid scattered its terrific fragments over the surface, but fortunately caused no other calamity than the most alarming fear amongst the inhabitants. But the most distressing part of the scene was at Plumtree Hospital. The poor residents there felt all the ill consequences of the pelting rain, the very beds of those who occupy the apartments below were literally swimming in water . . .'

22nd August 1802: Hurricane at Fledborough

The annals of the Nottinghamshire village of Fledborough record one of the most singular weather incidents of the early 19th century. Lydia, a member of the famous Penrose family who

27

were resident at the local parsonage, described the scene: '. . . for one instant eight of the largest plum trees, our South East Chimney, the lead covering of the Chancel, and several other trees, branches and different things were blown flat on the ground . . . This was instantaneous, but the hurricane lasted some minutes . . . It was a whirl-wind for the wind and rain went round and round . . . Papa all the while the hurricane lasted thought it seemed like as if we were blown away, by one puff of a bellows . . . it is a depressing sight to look out of the windows and see poor Fledborough the abomination of desolation. We have surely abundant cause for gratitude to Heaven that our lives were preserved. Had we not fortunately shut the windows about half an hour before the shock surprised us, I think nothing could have prevented our being crushed to atoms. You may conceive some idea of the fury of the storm from the lead of the Chancel about 2 tons weight, being carried by the wind upwards of 36 feet all in one mass.' (Extract from *The Penroses of Fledborough Parsonage* by A.B. Baldwin, 1933)

1803: The Weather and 'Derby Neck'

Climate profoundly influences lifestyles and culture. It also has a marked affect on health, a subject considered in its meteorological context by James Pilkington in his book *A View of the Present State of Derbyshire*, published in 1803.

Pilkington was very familiar with the precipitate wetness of Derbyshire, a smidgen of humour creeping into his otherwise measured scientific description of High Peak weather. 'Rain during the winter season frequently falling as snow, sleet and hail, cannot on account of the strong winds, which prevail here, be collected with so much accuracy.' The author goes on to suggest in his chapter on atmosphere and climate that altitude is generally associated with salubrity, although he qualifies his assertions by alluding to an affliction long peculiarly associated with a county from which it derives its name. 'Derby Neck' is dealt with at some length.

Greatly prevalent in Derbyshire, being observed from the Peak to Derby itself, the disease is described as a tumour 'arising on the fore-part of the neck'. Affecting girls almost exclusively (we are told that 'fifty poor girls' in the small village of Duffield were afflicted) Derby Neck is likened to the 'flap or dew-cap of a turkey cock's neck'. The suggested remedy for this malady makes the hair curl.

'Take Cinnabar of Antimony levigated, one seruple; woodlice prepar'd and powder'd, Burnt sponge, of each fifteen grains, to be made into a powder.'

The medicine was to be taken twice a day for two or three weeks, the dosing to be supplemented by the swallowing of three mercury pills. Derby Neck was seldom fatal . . . but the cure!

1811: The Weather of the High Peak

'A disposition to the marvellous seems to me to have pervaded all the accounts of the climate and surface of Derbyshire which I have read . . . The name High Peak seems almost generally misunderstood by strangers to Derbyshire, and even by a large proportion of the inhabitants of the county itself; the greater number understanding thereby a certain alpine and inhospitable region; while others have magnified the High Peak to refer to some frightful mountain or precipice, which like that of Tenerif, lorded it over all the surrounding country.' (*Agriculture and Minerals of Derbyshire* by John Farey, 1811)

1816: The Year Without a Summer

The summer of this thoroughly miserable year was one of the coldest ever recorded in mid-England. The unseasonal lack of

2. Rain.

By the kindness of His Grace of Devonshire, and of his Agent, Mr. Knowlton, of Edensor, I am enabled to present a very satisfactory abstract of the Rain which fell at Chatsworth during 50 years past, ascertained by an excellent and well-attended Rain-Guage in the Gardens at that place, the funnel of which seems to be about 18 feet above the Ground, and about 60 feet above the Derwent River at Chatsworth : the depth of Rain is registered by the Gardener every morning, at nine o'clock, which has fallen in the preceding Day and Night. The following are the yearly totals, viz. in 1761, 26.525 inches ; in 1762, 23.399 inches; and in

Years.	Inches.	Years.	Inches.	Years.	Inches.
1763	36.399	1779	24.582	1795	23.531
1764	34.262	1780	19.443	1796	24.280
1765	27.536	1781	23.065	1797	30.129
1766	25.235	1782	39.115	1798	27.562
1767	30.723	1783	29.526	1799	30.995
1768	39.919	1784	22.976	1800	27.732
1769	27.255	1785	23.162	1801	28.345
1770	29.446	1786	30.676	1802	23.340
1771	22.433	1787	32.068	1803	24.270
1772	30.842	1788	19.856	1804	47.904
1773	31.281	1789	36.309	1805	22.232
1774	31.522	1790	26.892	1806	30.182
1775	33.749	1791	34.698	1807	26.365
1776	29.892	1792	34.740	1808	28.509
1777	24.794	1793	24.316	1809	29 911
1778	29.895	1794	30.769	1810	27.984

Rain at Chatsworth, 1811. (From: Agriculture and Minerals of Derbyshire (Vol I) by John Farey)

sunlight and low temperatures can be reliably ascribed to the tremendous explosion in April 1815 of the Tamboro volcano in the East Indies. The eruption, which took seven months to reach maximum volcanic intensity and in total lasted 15 months, spewed millions of tons of ash into the atmosphere blocking out the sun, disrupting wind patterns, increasing the frequency of low pressure systems and rainfall across the globe. In Derbyshire particularly, conditions were dour. Snow fell in the county as late as June and in higher parts of the district unripe oat crops languished until October. The cold, wet and overcast conditions devastated the labour intensive farming industry and a third of the workforce was laid off putting intolerable strains on the workhouses and parish charities.

16th January 1852: Death in Matlock Bath

Benign ripples to deadly torrents, transformed in the bursting of a cloud. All watercourses in spate are dangerous places as this tragic account from 1852 shows.

After heavy rain, the swollen Derwent raced through its gorge in Matlock Bath, where stood a young boy entranced by the scene. A visitor to the town, the boy persuaded his father to hire a rowing boat and boldly they set out on their last journey.

Taking the oars, the father spurned warnings about the dangers of the south weir and declined the services of a river guide, explaining that he knew the river well. The boat was committed to the stream and on it went at the mercy of the current.

At a great rate of knots the flimsy craft approached the roaring Massons Weir on the Willersley side. Frantically the man tried to row away from the cauldron of water but his efforts were to no avail. The boat struck the weir rocks and became lodged in a crevice. On the bank, alarmed observers sent for a rope and the occupants of the boat were signalled to remain still. Despite the desperate situation, reckless confidence again held sway and taking the child in his arms, the man elected to wade to safety.

Fighting the torrent, the man struggled to reach the Matlock Bath bank, a full 60 yards distant. Weighed down by his son he battled valiantly but again and again he was knocked over by the sheer power of the river. He struggled to his feet one last time, vomiting water. Then he was gone, the terrified lad still clinging to his breast.

Although the river was dragged soon after the tragedy the bodies remained in the water for 14 days. Eventually the corpses were found near the Derwent's confluence with the Lea Brook. The man left a wife and seven other children.

9th May 1853: Snow Dust

So fine was the snow that descended on Derbyshire on the 9th May 1853 that it penetrated some parlours and bedrooms, blowing through keyholes and under doors and accumulating in drifts over a foot deep. A south-west wind drove obscuring clouds of minute, particled snow into huge drifts up to 15 feet deep, blocking roads and cutting off villages. The density of the blizzard was so pronounced that coachmen peered in vain for sight of their horses. Embedded in a drift with his heavy vehicle, one man came to grief on Fairfield Common.

24th February 1855: Tricky Wicket

Determined to enjoy the excesses of the English winter, a group of fun loving stoics took part in an hilarious cricket match played on the frozen Trent at Fiskerton. With several skaters in their team, the eleven from Fiskerton and Morton trounced the opposition from Stoke and Elston by 21 runs. And did the ball run! To celebrate the victory, a whole sheep was roasted on the ice.

A month later as the thaw set in, a mini iceberg estimated at several tons in weight destroyed the old bridge at Kelham. A large body of men attempted to fend off the leviathan with props and stout poles but it smashed against the piles and caused the structure to collapse. Five laden carts crossed the bridge in the nick of time although one pedestrian nearly lost his life through hesitation. His dilemma was which way to run. As the ice struck he decided on the Newark side and made it with only seconds to spare.

June 1859: Miraculous Escape in Breadsall

'Sir,
Yesterday morning about 8 o'clock when the storm was at its height, the lightning struck a house in the village of Breadsall with such a force as almost to demolish it. The electric fluid seems to have first entered one of the bedrooms through the roof where it exploded blowing the window out, smashing all the furniture and setting the bed on fire. In this room the man and his wife slept but most providentially they were both up. The fluid afterwards passed through the wall to the next chamber where a little girl was in bed but strange to say though it broke the wall close to her head and knocked the window out she was not the least injured. It afterwards went down through the floor into the house place where another girl was sitting. She was knocked down but with the exception of some slight burns on the neck is not hurt. The mother who was outside the door was knocked down but not hurt. The house, a modern brick building is shaken to pieces, the walls cracked and the windows at the front blown out. Perhaps there was never known such a wholesale destruction of a house by lightning and yet such

providential and miraculous preservation of the inmates.

I remain, Sir, Yours faithfully,

Henry R. Crewe, Breadsall Rectory, 27th June 1859'

'PS   To show the force of the explosion, I am told that pieces of the tiles of the roof were hurled 50 yards. This house, which is one of a row of five, seemed to have sustained the whole force of the shock as none of the others were touched.'

(Letter to *Derby and Chesterfield Reporter*)

10th June 1860: Twin Thunderbolts

As residents prepared for Sunday worship, Chesterfield was assailed by a tremendous electrical storm. Heavy rain and thunder and lightning inflicted considerable damage on garden crops and some stampeded livestock perished. Derbyshire's premier landmark, the twisted spire of Chesterfield parish church, suffered badly as a consequence of twin lightning strikes.

Shortly before the commencement of morning service, a vivid flash of lightning, accompanied by loud peals of thunder illuminated the nave startling the entire congregation. The Revd G. Butt, incumbent, and an assembly of the Chatsworth Rifles, felt the full shock of the strike and several of the men were much alarmed. Although disrupted, the service continued.

'Electric fluid', according to a contemporary newspaper account, 'entered the tower of the church and destroyed the brass wires used for communicating with the ringers before the commencement of Divine Service and cut them in a number of places and twisted them after the fashion of a corkscrew. The west face of the clock, a portion of which was composed of glass, was also broken.'

23rd October 1872: An Inland Sea

Over the centuries, Trent floods have been as regular as the effects of senna pods and prunes. Draining a vast tract of land, this great river has frequently broken its banks, spreading misery and destruction far and wide.

Precariously sited, Nottingham has suffered for its impudence with a series of inundations, catalogued in the annals of each generation, as rich a tribute to fortitude, endurance and courage as any tales from Sherwood. In such respect, newspaper accounts of the great flood of 1872 are worthy of note.

Describing the Trent after heavy rain, a *Nottingham Journal* columnist reported . . . 'nothing scarcely, save the picture of ships in the distance, caused it to differ from the sea. The floods caused great privation and danger but neighbourliness, courage and improvisation saved the day. Provisions were conveyed to stranded residents in Queens Walk and Trent Lane by boat. In the fast current, there was an exciting recovery of an errant stone ladened barge at Holme Pierrepont and an equally stirring rescue of a number of drowning cattle by passers by on the flooded pastures between the Wilford and the Trent bridges. We hope,' said our reporter 'that the men who thus saved the lives of the cattle at the risk of their own were suitably rewarded.' Pigs were also saved from death. 'The more humane of the pig-owners,' continues the account, 'after having rescued the grunters from the water, conveyed them in triumph into the houses until such time as the floods should abate.' Mother would have been pleased! With great gravity, the scribe also records the effect of the flood on the cellars of a public house near Queens Walk. 'The water has made sad havoc . . . and a good deal of malt liquour therein contained has been diluted even more than the landlord himself would wish.' And devotion to duty by purveyors of the peace was exemplary. As rabbits and hares climbed trees to escape the water, gamekeepers patrolled their territories by boat!

Skating at Trent Bridge, Nottingham, February 1895. (Terry Goodlud)

29th October 1880: Not a Drop to Drink

Millions of gallons of water swamped Nottinghamshire towns and villages following three days of heavy rain, the rivers Soar, Trent and Leen and numerous smaller streams and tributaries bursting their banks. From Retford, where shops and foundries were brought to a standstill, to Nottingham centre, it was a soggy tale of rescue and ruination.

Ever vulnerable Nottingham suffered badly, marooned residents in Cremorne Street, Clayton Street, Wilford Road and Deering

Street suffering a titanic inrush of water that sent some people splashing for their lives in water up to eight ft deep. But the flood had a silver lining. Resourceful shopkeepers including butchers, bakers and provision dealers, realising the potential for increased sales, hired boats and plied their trades as gondoliers. Generally, however, the floods brought only heartache and despair, although there were no fatalities like those experienced in the catastrophe of July 1875.

Many suburbs, hamlets and villages were visited by the inexorable floods, Attenborough, Beeston, Basford, Bulwell, Radcliffe, Gunthorpe, Hoveringham, Hazleford and Kegworth all reporting damage and disruption. Burton Joyce was completely surrounded by water and at Shelford, a desperate gang of men worked feverishly to strengthen the river bank fearing a catastrophic burst.

List of notable 19th century Trent Bridge Floods

The heights of the floods in feet above mean sea level were: –

1852 (November)	79.37
1857	77.38
1864 (March)	77.13
1869 (December)	78.45
1875 (July)	77.95
1875 (October)	79.70
1886 (May)	78.65

1895: A Foul Frost

Lasting from early January until late February, a bone cracking frost held England in its grip. Throughout the land there were extraordinary accounts of frozen rivers, ice floes and ice-bound creeks and jetties and there were widespread reports of mass lay-offs in industry.

For a time, the Thames was blocked by ice floes up to seven ft thick. In Oxford a coach and six was driven over the frozen river Cherwell and in the twin counties many watercourses froze solid from bank to bank.

The most severe of the 'nights of intense keenness' were those between 5th and the 11th February, the temperature remaining below freezing throughout the daylight hours. On 8th February at Belper the thermometer showed the lowest reading ever recorded in south-east Derbyshire ($-15.9\,°C$), the extreme cold at night coupled with sunny daytime conditions allowed capital sport on ponds, reservoirs and rivers.

Skaters turned out in force on the Derwent and the Trent and a hockey match was played between teams from Newark and Burton above Averham Weirs. Hundreds of other people 'disported themselves on the ice'. But there was great hardship. Hundreds of people were thrown out of work and there was a shortage of food and fuel. The public spirited Lord Mayor of Newark, however, took a prominent lead in his determination to alleviate suffering. He called a public meeting to exhort Nottinghamshire citizens to contribute to a hardship fund and over £300 was raised, 'a generosity excelled by no other town in England'. Wildlife also suffered. Songbird populations were decimated and coveys of half-starved grouse deserted the moors and descended on Matlock Bath in a desperate search for food.

19th Century Spits and Spots

1816: An earthquake shook Mansfield. Worshippers in the parish church bolted for the door and in the mêlée many people were injured.

The frozen Trent, February 1895. (Terry Goodlud)

1821: A tremendous bolt of lightning struck the Holy Cross church at Epperstone, Nottinghamshire, severely damaging the spire and the clock.

1826: An opportunity was taken during a protracted drought to examine and repair the bridge at Nottingham. The masons discovered fragments of sculptured stone, parts of mullion windows ascribed to the ancient chapel of St Mary which was once built on the bridge.

On the 1st July, hailstones, some larger than goose eggs, pelted South Wingfield in Derbyshire. Despite the high temperatures, some hailstones remained frozen for four days.

1829: The monumental *History, Gazetteer, and Directory of the County of Derby* described fearsome spates of the river Dove. 'These floods are, however, sometimes so sudden, that the waters have been known to rise and fall in the course of a day, carrying down their channel flocks of sheep and herds of cattle. Such inundations are caused by what are termed "shots of water", which the Dove often receives in its course through the mountains.'

1836: Poor families in the Nottingham area welcomed the heavy Christmas snowfalls. Drifts up to window-sill height blocked the roads and gave much needed work to hundreds of men. Housewives rejoiced 'because of the excellent wages the shovellers received at a season when employment was scarce'.

1846: 'The winter of 1846 was very extraordinary. Up to the middle of March there was no cold, the cuckoo was heard in Derbyshire and a swarm of bees seen in Hampshire; then from the middle of March, snow and rain, and the ice-house was filled on the 21st March, and the white-thorns round the ice-house were in leaf and showing flowers. Nobody remembers such a winter.' (Extract from the diary of Mrs Harriot Munday, Lady of the Manor at Markeaton, Derby)

EARLY TWENTIETH CENTURY

Weather Notes 1901 – 1927

1901: Buxton experienced remarkable extremes of temperature with a winter low of – 18.3°C, contrasting sharply with the summer high of 31.1°C.

1903: On the 24th March, an earthquake rocked Matlock Bath and adjoining parishes.

1910: Incessant rain and heavy falls of snow combined to flood the whole of the Trent valley. The Midland railway line from Attenborough to Nottingham station was submerged in feet of water and hard pressed steam engines had to battle to maintain services.

1911: Summer was the hottest in the region since 1868, Derby sweltering in a temperature of 34.2°C on the 9th August. On the same day, Kew in London recorded the highest temperature ever in Britain, 100°F. An observer in St James's Park during the afternoon of that day related how, like Arthur Askey many years later, he watched the flowers fading 'before his very eyes'! During that remarkable summer, a terrific thunderstorm tore down the pinnacle of the village church at Old Brampton on the edge of the Peak District. Inverted on a plinth, the dislodged stone made an admirable bird bath.

1916: In January, taking advantage of light airs, Zeppelins raided Chesterfield. Heavy snow fell in the Pennines in March, ten ft drifts closing the High Peak Railway. On 3rd September, Nottingham was bombarded with hailstones, some up to 1.25 inches in diameter.

1917: On All Fools Day, the temperature plunged to − 14°C in Worksop. Kew Gardens meanwhile did not report a frost. On 2nd April, the thermometer dropped to − 10°C in Belper, the coldest April night recorded there in over a century. The protracted winter extended into May. During the mediocre summer, incessant rain in Flanders turned the battlefield at Ypres into a quagmire.

1919: During the Armistice Day services on the 11th November, the Peak District had the heaviest snowfalls in 40 years.

1921: Derbyshire experienced an exceptionally dry start to the summer. In June it rained on just three days, the afternoon temperature averaging 78°F.

1922: May was the exception in a Derbyshire summer marked by unseasonal cold. During the past 114 years, the summer of 1922 ranks alongside those of 1888 and 1907 as the coldest.

1926: A curious hailstorm bombarded Derby on the 14th May. The whole of the southern half of the town was covered in a crunchy mantle. Pavements in the northern area remained dry. Throughout the five minute storm, a valiant policeman remained on point duty at the junction of Cornmarket and St James's Street . . . legends and ballads are made of this.

Lightning, torrential rain and hailstones accompanied by hurricane force winds terrorised inhabitants in the High Peak on the 19th July. The thunderstorm was the worst in 20 years.

1927: Crowds assembled in St Thomas's Road, Derby, in the early hours of the 29th June to witness a total eclipse of the sun. Jockeying for the best positions, gazers raised pieces of smoked glass at 4.47 am to witness a phenomenon which will not recur until August 1999.

April 1905: A Rude Awakening

In the early hours of a late April Sunday, sleepers throughout Nottinghamshire were awakened by an earthquake. Two distinct tremors were felt, each lasting up to ten seconds and each accompanied by thunderous noises, variously described as being like that of a 'heavy road locomotive' or that resembling the fall 'of a heavy load of furniture.'

In Nottingham, doors and windows rattled violently, crockery was dashed to the ground and the Bath Street police station was shaken as though 'a heavy vehicle was passing', the on-duty sergeant rushing outside to ascertain the cause. Residents of Newark also felt the shocks, described as 'more an upheaval than an oscillation from side to side – a direct lifting up rather than a tremulous shake'. In Ollerton, Retford and Worksop there was similar alarm, some people running to their neighbours half naked and some becoming ill as a consequence of their great fright.

6th and 7th Agust 1922: Mops Aready!

Contemporary photographs of the aftermath of a deluge at Radcliffe-on-Trent show a bevy of mopsters removing 'mud and water which had entered their house to the depth of nearly four feet'. And they are all beaming – smile, girls! Notwithstanding the problems brought by unrelenting rain, humour was prominent in local newspaper accounts, one report describing the typically British phlegm and pragmatism of a stranded Radcliffe motorist whose automobile came to a stop in the deep flood water. The driver was a city gent whose spats were not for splashing, so he stripped naked, held his clothes aloft and waded to dry land. Unfortunately the cameraman missed that one!

In other Nottinghamshire districts there was little levity. Mansfield registered a local rainfall record over the two days of 4.34 inches and many houses were flooded in Retford.

At Pinxton near Alfreton and the Nottinghamshire/Derbyshire boundary, persistent heavy rain led to the overflow of the Erewash and large crowds assembled around the factory yard and the Great Northern Station to witness what were unprecedented floods. Some old folk whose homes in Meadow Row and nearby streets were up to five ft deep in water retreated to upstairs rooms and emergency supplies had to be ferried in.

THE WEATHER IN
THE THIRTIES

3rd September 1931: Derbyshire Deluge

Massive cloudbursts brought flood chaos across the county. Derby residents in the low lying Brook Street, Brook Walk and Searl Street areas near to the notoriously flood prone Markeaton Brook were marooned and had to retreat to upper rooms. Markeaton recreation ground was transformed into a lake and vegetables washed from the nearby allotments floated in the streets.

Newly formed rivers all along the Derwent valley demolished walls, tore up road surfaces, disrupted road and rail transport, caused local power failures and fractured water mains. Switch box fusing plunged Mackworth, Kirk Langley, Quarndon and Kedleston into darkness. Between Mickleover and Etwall, a railway line was washed away and even the rats were hard pressed in Ilkeston and Heanor, hundreds of the vermin swimming for their lives in flooded streets.

The flood waters played havoc with commercial establishments. In a water filled cellar, Mr A. Blackburn, a pork butcher in the Matlock area, lost 600 pounds of lard, several sides of bacon and other valuable foodstuffs. Other traders were in a similar plight.

The A6 flooded at Milford, May 1932. Intrepid Derby Telegraph reporter, suitably shod, interviews the flood victims (Derby Evening Telegraph)

The Henmore river near Ashbourne and the Hipper at Chesterfield both overflowed, the latter inundating the Robinson weaving mills where 300 of the workforce were temporarily made idle.

One Derby family enjoyed a toothsome end to their ordeal. Mr Jack Merry of Little Bridge Street discovered a pike floundering in a grate cover at the corner of Willow Row. Baked pike needs no lard!

23rd May 1932: Four Million Tons of Rain... and Some

Such was the astounding quantity of rain that drenched Derby and Nottingham on that never to be forgotten weekend, that

Cornmarket, Derby, 22nd May 1932. (Douglas Farnsworth)

1932 ranks alongside 1947 as the most prominent local weather year of the twentieth century.

All over England, May 1932 was the wettest for 160 years. Continuous heavy rain over the whole region brought a massive and a relentless rise in water levels affecting the entire drainage system and there was catastrophic flooding over a wide area. In

Topical sketches, Nottingham Evening News, 24th May 1932.
(Nottingham Evening News)

just two days, Belper recorded total rainfall of 3.34 inches. Both Nottingham and Derby and scores of smaller towns and villages were drowned in torrents of water.

Residents of Ilkeston witnessed a tragic drowning when a child of seven fell into the swollen Erewash. The racing river Ryton in Worksop caused havoc when it surrounded the post office and the hospital and rushed into the picture house and covered the seats. Further south, hundreds of acres of farmland around Nottingham were inundated, scores of helpless cattle being swept along by the racing current. Nearby, Long Eaton, Wilford and West Bridgford fared particularly badly, boat owners doing sterling work in ferrying supplies and rescuing the sick and the infirm. In marooned West Bridgford, there were amazing scenes as two girls donned bathing costumes and swam one and a half miles to work. And in flooded streets near Trent Bridge, fun loving pranksters used the roofs of submerged cars as diving boards! All transport systems were disrupted. Miles of roads were impassable and such was the ingress of water into the Nottingham LMS railway station that it resembled a dock. But the mails got through – stranded residents in Gunthorpe had their letters delivered by speed boat!

Industry and commerce fared little better. Pit shaft seepage led to a stoppage of work at Clifton colliery and the *Daily Telegraph* print room in Derby was put out of action when three ft of water short-circuited the presses. But the *Derby Daily Express* kept rolling, its banner headline for the 23rd revealing a city-wide damage bill of £400,000.

March 1933: Sky High Trent

Thawing snow in the Derbyshire hills brought familiar tragedy to the flood plain of the Trent, the water-gorged river rising to an incredible 77.63 ft above mean sea-level at Trent Bridge on the 1st March. Surveying the scene from an aeroplane, a Nottingham pilot reported massive flooding at Sawley and at Attenborough. He flew on into Derbyshire, inspected the swollen river Manifold and continued to Ashbourne and the hills to the north where still-frozen snow threatened further catastrophe. 'Quite the worst flood I found during my flight was between Shardlow and Nottingham,' said the pilot on returning to his Tollerton base.

Once again, a year on from the flooding of 1932, Wilford endured terrible incursions of the Trent. The main street was awash and the road between the toll bridge and the Ferry Inn was so deep in water and the currents so treacherous that it was impassable to traffic. Elsewhere in the village, asphalt was stripped from the road surface by the force of the water and the school was inundated giving an unexpected holiday for Wilford children. In the Buxton district of Derbyshire, flooded roads hampered the Royal Mail and letters were delivered on horseback.

Floods in Bridge Street, Long Eaton, May 1932. (Mrs J Williams)

Thirties Miscellany

1930: Across the country on the 12th January, twelve people were killed in gales. A gust of 102 mph was recorded in Falmouth. Derbyshire suffered only minor damage but there was a near fatality in Chapel Street, Derby where a tumbling gable end narrowly missed the proprietor of a shop.

Two inches of rain fell in 50 minutes in the Peak District on the 18th June. Torrential rain and vivid lightning visited Matlock.

1931: A heatwave in May melted many tar-covered roads in Derby. Swimmers cooled off in the Derwent.

A storm of amazing intensity swept Derby and district on the 14th June. Hundreds of excursionists were caught in the deluge. Huge hailstones fell on Welbeck Abbey, trees were blown down in Chaddesden Park and telephone wires were damaged at Ashbourne, Brailsford, Ambergate and Bakewell.

Derby Road, Long Eaton, May 1932. Barton's service bus on route no.5 – Nottingham to Derby. (Mrs J Williams)

Floods in Derby Road, Long Eaton, May 1932. (Mrs J Williams)

1932: East Bridgford on the Trent suffered one of the worst downpours in its history – 2.96 inches of rain fell on the 13th July.

On the 9th and 10th July, temperatures across the two counties reached the low 80s. One of the hottest weekends for years brought out the crowds. Buses bound for Buxton, Dovedale, Alton Towers and Matlock were packed. Hundreds of picnic parties were reported on the upper reaches of the Derwent and the river gardens at Belper 'presented a gay scene'.

1933: Floodlight skating was the main attraction at Alvaston Lake on the 27th January. The blades were also out in force on frozen reservoirs in the Ripley district. The use of motor vehicle headlights allowed midnight sport on the Lodge Farm Pond at Long Eaton.

A fireball struck St Christopher's church in Derby on the 20th June splitting its bell arch cross.

As a remarkable contrast to the floods of March, drought conditions prevailed in the Trent valley, the low waters revealing a Roman ford at the village of Littleborough on the Lincoln to Doncaster road. Prolonged rather than hot, the summer earned the distinction of being the warmest in the region since 1911.

1935: Dense fog and bitter cold depressed Christmas sales in Derby and Nottingham shops but a rise in temperatures on the 24th brought a late rush of shoppers.

A post-Christmas Trent flood dampened festivities in Gunthorpe. Parents attending a Sunday school prize giving and nativity play carried children aloft to keep them dry. Thawing snow and heavy rain caused extensive flooding in Derbyshire. Hundreds of acres of farmland were submerged between

Shardlow and Sawley. Settlements alongside the river Dove, particularly Doveridge and Sudbury, fared badly.

Total October rainfall at Barrow Clough in the High Peak was 14.64 inches.

1936: In December, seven RAF Heyfords on a flight from Northern Ireland to Finningley in Yorkshire ran into bad weather over the Peak District. Six aircraft were forced down and three crew members died. At the time this was the service's worst peacetime disaster.

1938: For once, Bing Crosby's dream came true, when snow fell in the region on Christmas Eve.

THE WEATHER IN
THE FORTIES

9th February 1946: Terrible Trent

Prolonged rainstorms brought further flood torment to long-suffering residents in the Trent Bridge, West Bridgford and Wilford areas. Topping the 1932 flood level, the Trent poured into homes sending occupants scurrying upstairs for safety. Some were marooned for days without power. Emergency deliveries of food, coal, soap and disinfectant had to be provided by the authorities who were severely criticised for the lack of adequate warning and for failure to implement flood protection works.

At the height of the flood, road access to Nottingham was cut from the south and east and the waters reached platform height in parts of the LMS railway station and sidings. Answering a call from bedimmed constabulary in the Queens Drive police station, Guildhall officials sent lanterns and 40 pairs of wellingtons, essential equipment for the planned rescue of two youths who shinned up a tree in East Stoke after their canoe capsized. In Long Eaton inflatable RAF boats were deployed in delivering essential foodstuffs to trapped residents.

One marooned gentleman, a naval stoker resident of Wilford Lane, Nottingham, saw the funny side of his predicament. Evacuated by boat on the appropriately aquatic first leg of his

Ruddington bus stranded in Wilford Lane opposite Wilford allotments, 1946. (Mr G Mann)

Melton Road, West Bridgford, 1946. (Mr G Mann)

The return of the empty bottle saves coal because coal is used in the manufacture of new bottles.
Office's Brewery, Limited

DERBY EVENING TELEGRAPH

INCORPORATING THE DERBY DAILY EXPRESS

LATE FINAL

Hancocks Tel. 1128
15, CURZON ST.

VOL. CXIX.—No. 20,421   TUESDAY, FEBRUARY 4, 1947   THREE HALFPENCE

*Towns And Villages Isolated: Passengers Stranded All Night In Trains:
Buses Abandoned On Moors: Roads Blocked By 10-Ft. Drifts*

BLIZZARD'S MASS HOLD-UP
IN DERBYSHIRE

SCORES of Derbyshire towns and villages were to-day cut off completely by snowdrifts from ten to 12 feet deep and from all parts of the county came stories of marooned buses and mail vans, dislocated road and rail transport and stranded lorries and cars.

Buxton, and practically every village in its vicinity, became cut off by road and rail late yesterday afternoon, following a 12-hour blizzard, and was still isolated to-day. Passenger trains from Manchester were marooned at Dove Holes throughout the night.

A NUMBER of villages in the Belper-Ashbourne, Ashbourne-Derby area were also Uttoxeter, Ashbourne - Leek, marooned although snowploughs Derby-Holbrook, Ashbourne-and gangs of County Council Sudbury, Melbourne-Ashby, Melworkmen had been working all bourne-Swadlincote and Dufnight in a losing battle to keep field-Wirksworth roads were the roads clear. among the scores reported impassable this morning.

Ashbourne, Baslow, Crich, Longford, Parwich, Wirksworth, Hartington, Elton, Bradley, Winster, Thorpe and Ilam were among the many places reported isolated to-day.

On with the mail.—MRS. WALLACE, 63-years-old postwoman at Kirk Langley, was out early to-day delivering letters to isolated farms.

PANTO PARTIES' ALL
NIGHT IN BUSES

Three buses containing 78 women and children, who were stranded all night in the snow at Newbould, near Market Weighton, Yorks., were reached by gangs of workmen early this afternoon.

THEY left Hull yesterday afternoon to go to a pantomime at Leeds, about 60 miles away. On the return the buses became stranded in snowdrifts six to ten feet deep.

Another Leeds pantomime party consisting of 22 Whitby people were stranded all night when their motor coach stuck in snowdrifts on the moors near Lockton, on the Whitby-Pickering road.

The Outlook—

CONTINUING cold with occasional rain, sleet or snow in many districts, but temperature mainly a little above freezing. Strong east wind.

A.T.S. girls and a number of men travelling between Rochdale and Oldham spent the night in a train which ran into a snowdrift.

No buses were available to take hundreds of factory workers to the Trading Estates at Aycliffe and Bishop Auckland.

NO RAIL TRAFFIC

The mail train from Darlington to Crook arrived three hours late and there was no rail traffic between Crook and Tow Law.

Farmers in outlying places had to resort to hand feeding and many were searching for lost sheep.

No mails or newspapers had arrived at Bridlington by 9.15 a.m.

The Scarborough-Bridlington and the Leeds-Bridlington roads were blocked.

Binbrook, near Market Rasen, was the largest village in the Lincolnshire Wolds, was cut off by drifts 10ft. and 12ft. deep and snow was still falling.

In the Manchester, Sheffield, Leeds, Grimsby and Grantham

The R.A.C. reports that all roads in the north and North-east isolated spots to pick up workmen early to-day were left stranded in snow drifts. At Shottle a bus is stuck in a four-feet snow drift and the wheels of another are buried in snow at Hazlehurst.

A Trent bus travelling from Manchester to Derby last night stuck in a snow drift on Swinscoe Hill and passengers were taken to nearby houses where they were given food and put up for the night.

Many Buses
Abandoned

Trent buses attempting to reach isolated spots to pick up workmen early to-day were left stranded in snow drifts.

CLOCKED OUT

MANY of Derby's public clocks were snowed up to-day. The Town Hall clock stopped at 6.25 last night and refused to move again until this afternoon.

Five Midland General buses were snowbound all night on the moors between Matlock and Alfreton, and it was impossible to reach them this morning.

Services on this route are suspended, but it is hoped that some buses will be able to run later to-day between Alfreton and Chesterfield by diverting the route through Pilsley.

L.M.S. services were badly affected by the snow.

Thousands of gallons of water from melted snow on Dartmoor flooded streams and rivers. In the low-lying town of Newton Abbot doors and cellar entrances were barricaded last night. Shop-keepers plied provisions and wares on to counters and shelves in case the River Lemon, which flows through the town, flooded.

In the Chesterfield to Mansfield services have been cancelled. The company's snowploughs was out all night and kept other routes open. All services are retarded.

FLOOD FEARS

Turn To Back Page

Clearing the way for the snow plough to operate. Squads of workmen were busy on the main Ashbourne road between Kirk Langley and Brailsford to-day; like many roads in Derbyshire, it was impassable to motor traffic.

ELECTRICITY
CUTS HIT
DERBY

HOMES in Allenton were without electricity to-day when Derby Corporation power station reduced its load by ten per cent.

Reductions were also made by Burton Corporation and Derbyshire and Notts Electric Power Company's power stations.

A ten per cent. electricity cut started at 7.50 a.m. to-day over the whole of Britain, except the North-West area, where the reduction was five per cent.

An official of the Central Electricity Board described the cut as being "not quite so bad."

Snow drifted feet deep on the exposed Derbyshire roads. This photograph was taken near Ashbourne.

Battle Over
Transport
Bill Opens

THE Opposition assault on the Transport Bill was launched when the House of Commons Standing Committee to-day held its first meeting to consider the Bill.

Supporting Sir David Maxwell Fyfe (Con., West Derby), in a demand that the number of members of the Transport Commission should be increased from the proposed four to eight—excluding the chairman—Colonel J. R. H. Hutchison (Con., Glasgow Cen.) said: "This is another case of overloading of Ministers—talented though they are. "Ministers are no supermen and it seems they are trying to do jobs that are far too large for them."

Conservative members unsuccessfully resisted a proposal by the Minister (Mr. Alfred Barnes) that the executive members should meet three times a week so as to make "special efforts to get through it in reasonable time."

British Exodus From
Palestine Begins

The evacuation from Palestine of nearly 2,000 British women and children and a number of "non-essential" men began in Jerusalem, Haifa, Tel-Aviv, and Jaffa this morning.

POLICE posts were established every mile along the road from Jerusalem to the terrorist under sentence of death, to-day received permission from the Palestine Supreme camp, where the evacuees will be sent to communicate privately with the Privy Council in London and at once sent a cable.

Headline making weather, Derby Evening Telegraph, 4th February 1947. (Derby Evening Telegraph)

journey to Chatham, he smiled, describing his rescue by a man he saw floating down the street... 'I shouted to him and he rowed across the front garden to the bedroom window... He rowed me along Wilford Lane as far as Loughborough Road.' The majority of similarly affected householders were less accepting of their tribulations.

A public protest meeting was held in Wilford Parish Hall in March to examine the lamentable inaction by Nottingham Corporation and the West Bridgford Urban Council. At a packed assembly, councillors were condemned for inadequate warnings and slow reactions to the plight of flood victims. 'Enough loudspeakers are available at election time, but not one could be found to alert people to the flood dangers' accused one speaker. 'People have seen their homes virtually destroyed by water' protested another, adding, 'Many people who have spent their life savings buying houses have suffered great loss.' Various protesters spoke passionately about the extent of the floods. 'It was up to the picture rails in Roland Avenue.' 'There has been water in my garden nine months out of twelve and I have done no gardening for three years.' 'I will pay not one penny in rates until something is done!' Tempers eventually subsided and resolutions were passed promising action.

1947: The Big Freeze

Grindingly long and punctuated by almost daily blizzards, the legendary winter of 1947 is regarded as one of the worst of the century, its bleakness exacerbated by food and fuel shortages following the recent war. The whole of Britain virtually ground to a halt, the meteorological conditions being compounded by absenteeism and strikes in the mining and power industries.

In homes across the two counties conditions were grim. Coal supplies ran out, fires were stoked with broken furniture and

Blasted weather. Waggon-mounted jet engine used to clear the High Peak railway line near Hartington, 1947. (Derby Evening Telegraph)

there was a run on candles as precious electricity supplies were eked out. Bread and fresh vegetables became scarce and families already inured to rationing were urged to economise further by Prime Minister Clement Attlee who addressed the nation on radio. Farm animal and wildlife fatalities were enormous. Hundreds of sheep were lost and in the depths of the chill, reports came in from Great Easton near Kettering that ravenous magpies had attacked cattle, tearing flesh from their backs.

Snowfall on Monday 6th January affected most of the country. At Temple Normanton near Chesterfield a lorry skidded and blocked the road, the first of a myriad such accidents which, as the winter ground on, led to almost total paralysis. The following day there was more snow especially in the Peak District where anxious shepherds had to rescue buried sheep. Then, beginning on the 11th January, there was a short and cruelly deceptive respite. The mild interlude, marked by a spring-like temperature of 57°F in Belper, was abruptly ended on Thursday 23rd January when there was a sharp frost. That weekend it snowed . . . and the blessed stuff kept coming . . . until March.

On the 26th January blizzards swept through Derbyshire and snow fell continuously in Nottinghamshire although there was little coverage in the local press. The following day in Spondon, workers at the British Celanese factory went on short time, fuel shortages being blamed for the shut down. Five lace manufacturers at Long Eaton also had to close. Just 24 hours later, winter tightened its grip and the weather was front page news again.

The intense cold silenced Big Ben. In Lincolnshire five desperate families isolated by deep drifts had bread delivered in ore tubs along a one and a half mile suspended cable and there was even snow in the normally mild Scilly Isles. Locally, blizzards restricted visibility to 30 yards in the Newark area, 50 patients were treated in Nottingham General Hospital for fall injuries and in Derby, the *Evening Telegraph* reported that the Antarctic was proving to be warmer than many parts of Europe!

In a desperate attempt to keep communication arteries open there was a mass mobilisation of prisoners of war and casual labour and factories hit by the fuel shortages began to close, one of the first victims being the massive brick and tile works in Bridgwater.

On the eighth day of the freeze on the 30 January, ice floes were reported in the sea at Whitstable in Kent and ale drinkers wept at the sight of frozen bottled beer in a Cornish pub. A lack of fuel closed the Raleigh Industries plant in Nottingham on the 31st January as 5,000 employees were sent home to huddle around meagre fires in the dark! That same day, Nottingham

59

experienced its most severe electricity cut, the all pervasive weather affecting even radio transmissions, the popular BBC 'At Your Request' musical programme (with Sandy Macpherson at the theatre organ) being one of the early casualties.

The war with the Axis powers was finished but the struggle with the weather was just beginning. People rallied to the task, sheer heroism, pluck and outstanding neighbourliness matching the Churchillian comradeship of the war years. Mrs Betsy Alsop of Hulland Village, Ashbourne, remembers the community spirit well. 'All the local men were called by the council to leave their jobs to help clear the roads. This was all done by hand and shovels – no mechanical diggers in those days. The strong north-east, gale force winds daily filled the roads. The men worked seven days a week for six weeks or more. Traffic was non-existent on the B-roads. The farmers were unable to get the milk collected; much was frozen in the churns; much also had to go down the drain, but we housewives had unlimited supplies of free milk which was appreciated by the workmen for plenty of hot drinks. We were walking on the tops of the hedges in many places. Younger folk trudged to Ashbourne (five miles) for bread. Also the daughter of the village squire – Miss Ann Mosley rode horseback over fields to the Hognaston bakers and brought as much bread back as she could carry and shared it out amongst the villagers. Groceries usually delivered by the Co-op from Derby were left at Muggington Cock Inn for anyone to collect if possible. This was an unforgettable year. Frost on the windows of the living-room never thawed day or night even with a good open fire burning.'

Mrs Nora Woodward of Ilkeston has similar memories. 'Father and I set out from Heanor in the hopes of getting to Biggin Grange (near Hartington). It was a nightmare journey after Cromford. Apparently the Italian POWs had cleared the Via Gellia – a single track with snow walls either side 14 ft high. Thankfully, we carried on and reached the Waterloo Inn, where we indulged in a warmer before going on foot walking on the stone walls which were all but hidden under snow. The farmer's wife had a hard time keeping them all fed. Plenty of milk at first and potatoes, swedes etc, even a lamb was killed for food.'

Villagers and town dwellers struggled on, and with the new month came a cautious optimism for an improvement in conditions. Blizzards brought disappointment, heartache and even death. Eight hours of continuous snow in the Peak District, with hedge high drifts, cut access to a number of villages and dozens of sheep suffocated. All roads to Edale and Buxton were impassable and the Woodhead Pass was blocked by ten ft of snow. Lifeline rail access to Buxton was severed on the 3rd February by deep drifts. Heroic efforts were made, using commandeered tractors, sledges, horses and sheepdogs in St Bernard mode, to rescue trapped families and to deliver food and mail. 'The postman got through!' became a defiant battle cry, the exploits of postman J.S. Powell, who with the help of students delivered letters by sledge to snowbound villagers in Stoney Middleton, stiffening the resolve.

The snow had a silver lining for some. Scores of winter sports enthusiasts enjoyed the near alpine ambience of the hills and 5,000 construction workers in Nottingham had a real bonus. Housing construction in the city was at a standstill but in spite of the enforced lay-offs, craftsmen still earned 2/6d an hour for a 32-hour idle week. 'Snow is a costly business for builders' said one sad employer.

The 10th of February: Prime Minister Attlee broadcast to the nation asking all two million unemployed men to report to local employment exchanges for snow clearing duties. On the 11th February, the Cabinet discussed the possibility of mobilising military flame throwers to assist in the clearance of railway lines and roads and a ban was declared on dog racing and on the publishing of periodicals after the 15th. Desperation set in. The stark headline in the *Nottingham Journal* on the 13th February read, 'Nation Today Put On War Footing.' And military aircraft were deployed to deliver food – the resultant crash of a heavily laden Halifax bomber saddened the whole nation.

Ten bombers were engaged in bringing relief to villages on the Staffordshire side of Dovedale, to the hamlet of Longnor in the upper reaches of the Manifold and Dove valleys and to other isolated settlements around Buxton. Over 27,000 pounds of margarine, flour, jam, sugar and tinned food were to be dropped by parachute, stranded villagers marking the drop sites with black crosses in the snow. Longnor received its largesse to loud applause, the whole community, all 400, turning out to cheer the canisters as they floated from the sky. But there was desolation on Mount Pleasant, Grindon Moor. Bound for a target zone at Butterton, one aircraft crashed and exploded on impact, killing the two man crew and six passengers and strewing sugar and flour into the snow.

For 13 days until the 17th February, the temperature in Nottingham never rose above freezing point. Desperately trying to keep warm, many people huddled around open gas ovens leaving the appliances to burn all night to avoid hypothermia and frozen pipes. A number of fatalities showed the folly of this practice and warnings were issued by the Gas Department. There was a little light relief on the 18th. The stoical inhabitants of Ashbourne went ahead with their annual Shrovetide football game . . . 'After fluctuating play over meadows deep in snow and in the icy waters of the Henmore, a wild scramble over the frozen Shaw Croft fish pond led the game back into the main streets.'

More blizzards followed on the 21st February and soon afterwards, the biggest ever local avalanche crashed down near the Snake Inn, depositing 30 ft high piles of snow and ice along a 400 yd stretch of road. Thirty degrees of frost in Nottingham on the 24th February caused ice floes to form on the Trent, but then a thaw set in on the 26th and it was fracture time on the ice and 24 hour shifts for busy plumbers.

Hopes soared in March with the promise by the Air Ministry of a general thaw. Wrong again! There were yet more blizzards on the 5th March and widespread traffic chaos in Nottinghamshire and Derbyshire. Gingerly, the Ministry withdrew its thaw forecast on the 6th! That happy Thursday was a special day for Mr and Mrs Stanley Drewett at the ancient Barrel Inn at Bretton between Great Hucklow and Eyam. Marooned in the upstairs room of the inn by window-high snow drifts for five weeks and three days, they were finally dug out.

Eventually, it did thaw. The snowdrops sheepishly peeped forth and the debate began about a victorious nation reduced to its knees by a little snow. Grave questions were asked about our unpreparedness in the House of Commons, Mr P. Noel-Baker, Secretary of State for Air, giving the most unequivocal parliamentary answer ever. 'To my regret, I must admit that the science of meteorology still leaves much to be desired (laughter and cheers).'

March 1947: The Big Thaw

What freezes in these so called temperate latitudes eventually thaws and the mother of all thaws came after one of the foulest winters ever. Gale force winds in the region on the 16th March swept in very mild air and the melting process began with torrents of water from the hills and fields augmented by copious amounts of rainfall – three and a half times the monthly average. Nottinghamshire and Derbyshire braced themselves for the inevitable – the F word – flood.

Across the country the inundations were of cataclysmic proportions. In London, incontinent Old Father Thames

Me and my gal . . . Nottingham's first drive-in cinema on the corner of Queens Road and Station Road, Beeston, March 1947. (P Pembleton)

unburdened a flow of water three miles wide below Chertsey Bridge. Numerous rivers, streams and canals in this region followed suit and on the 17th March many residents had a soggy breakfast. The river Erewash and the Grand Union canal burst their banks and Sandiacre and Stapleford were flooded. Sandiacre railway station was swamped and water poured into the Crossley-Premier engine factory. Five hundred employees were laid off. The nearby premises of the Lace Web Spring Company were similarly affected. That same day, German POWs dug through a 30 ft deep accumulated trough of snow in the Nibble Cutting to unblock the LMS line between Wirksworth and Longcliffe. So deep was the snow and so constricted the space, that working in teams of three spaced out on the bank, the

David Lane, Basford during the Leen floods, March 1947.
(Nottingham Evening Post)

Mrs Mattison of Queens Drive, Nottingham copes with a scullery
flood, March 1947. (Nottingham Evening Post)

Above: 'Watch out for the berg!' Jennison Street, Bulwell during the Leen floods, March 1947. (Nottingham Evening Post)

Below: Train at Basford level crossing, March 1947. (Nottingham Evening Post)

66

Lincoln Street, Old Basford during the Leen floods, March 1947. (Nottingham Evening Post)

The famous picture of Lionel Trinder outside 104 Queens Drive, Nottingham, March 1947. He went on to circumnavigate the globe! (Nottingham Evening Post)

diggers had to pass snow from man to man until it was shovelled clear. At lower levels, the thaw was gathering pace.

By the 20th of March, Nottingham was virtually cut off from the south and east; the closest river crossings were at Newark and Swarkestone. Around one eighth of the city area was flooded. Twenty-eight miles of streets were deep in water. Four thousand homes and 4,000 non-residential properties were affected. So much for the bald statistics. What of the misery?

The Meadows area was devastated. 'We lived in a part of the Meadows that never got flooded' recalls Mrs S. Davis. 'That's why my gran came to stop with us. It was quite a shock to wake up surrounded by water. We had to cook on a small coal fire in the bedroom for about a week, but the baker and the milkman never failed to turn up.'

The whole Embankment playing fields were covered by water and the War Memorial Park was one vast lake. The Midlands railway station had water up to the platforms and the Royal Ordnance factory was also swamped. In the Dunkirk district the flood spread as far as Abbey Bridge. Small boats were commandeered by the local constabulary from Highfields Boating Lake and at a nearby barrel factory, workers switched production to rafts! The University Rowing Club did sterling work in delivering supplies and two local bobbies and a certain Sergeant Farnsworth were also prominent in ferrying relief.

'Patrolling their beat by boat' the policemen delivered ten stones of bread and 200 bottles of milk to islanders in the Harrimans Street and Gibbons Street areas. But then the boat got stuck in a hedge top! A lasso and an effective Roy Rodgers impersonation and all was well. The boat continued its rounds, although the crew had to crouch in the scuppers to prevent bumping their heads on the bridge in Montpelier Road!

Three men and a boat. Sergeant Porter, PC Whitt and one able-bodied passer-by preparing for launch in Montpelier Road, Dunkirk, Nottingham, March 1947. (Nottingham Evening Post)

The floods caused an abiding mystery for former bus driver George Sheard of Arnold. 'My driver and I were on route 14 to Ruddington with a Guy double deck bus with a back platform which had a bar down the centre to help people on and off. Well, in 1947 we were trying to get to Ruddington via Wilford village which was submerged due to the river Trent bursting its banks. All the houses and bungalows were under water and we could go no further. What passengers we had, paddled the rest of the way home and my driver and I left the bus partially submerged. Several days later a gang of fitters went out to retrieve it by towing – when low and behold – a huge tree was embedded inside the bus. The mystery is, how did the tree get by the centre pole?'

The Roaring Forties

1940: The first winter of the war was the worst in the region since 1895, the cold spell lasting throughout January and the first three weeks of February. The river Trent froze over at Shardlow and barges in the fleet of the Trent Navigation Company were imprisoned by the ice. On the night of the 21st January the temperature at Belper plummeted to − 17.8°C. On the 26th of January, much of Derbyshire was mantled with up to two ft of undrifted snow. In the harsh conditions, many birds and animals died. To confuse the enemy, all weather reports were censored during January, newspaper and wireless commentaries being postponed for 15 days. In the same month, the War Office announced the suspension of home leave for the British Expeditionary Force as a consequence of the severe weather conditions.

In June, Buxton enjoyed a record tally of 273.5 hours' sunshine.

1944: A very mild, largely frost free winter in Nottinghamshire went out with a flourish on the 26th February, when up to 12 inches of snow fell in the Nottingham and Mansfield areas.

1947: The region basked under compensatory hot summer skies. In June, temperatures nudged the 90s and August was particularly hot.

1949: Wirksworth returned a record temperature for July of 88°F. Drought conditions persisted across the country. Sun parched vegetation was susceptible to fire and sparks from steam locomotives caused a number of blazes. The fitting of spark arresters failed to solve the problem.

THE WEATHER IN
THE FIFTIES

19th May 1952: The Tibshelf Tornado

The peaceful mining village of Tibshelf near to the eastern boundary of Derbyshire was ill-prepared for the devastating visitation that roared from a darkening sky at 3 o'clock on that fateful May afternoon. Tracking generally north-south from Hardstoft to Tibshelf, the tornado clove a trail of destruction, damaging over 100 houses and plucking mature trees from the ground. Aileen Hill, the daughter of W.H. Hill of Tibshelf who witnessed the spectacle, has sent me a copy of her late father's account: 'It was very hot in the sun. About 14.30 GMT the sky began to darken . . . The calmness was then suddenly broken by a single lightning flash and crack of thunder . . . we immediately left the field on a tractor . . . About four minutes later the tornado was in full blast at the cedars, and at the point we had just left. At the same time there was a shower of large raindrops and hailstones of various sizes, some egg-shaped or elongated, and the largest five-eighths of an inch across at the widest part. A great roaring noise, something like the continuous roar of a great waterfall, could now be heard, apparently coming from the vicinity of Hurst Lodge, to the west of which we could see all the trees in violent turmoil, branches being wrenched off, flung upwards into the air, and whirled around with other debris . . .' Mr. Hill wisely retreated to his house at this stage.

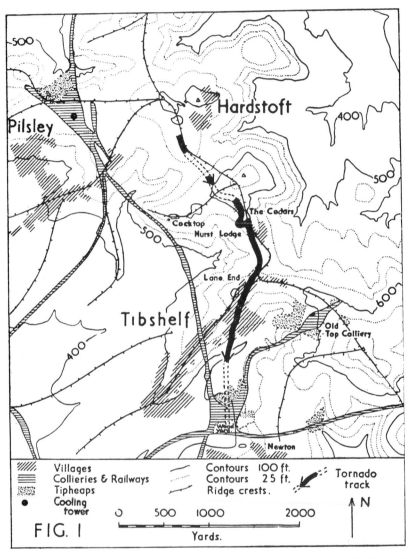

Plan showing the track of Tibshelf tornado, 19th May 1952. (Royal
Meteorological Society and Weather magazine)

'I ran upstairs to close an open window to check the through draught, and was able to get a full view of the action of the vortex, which roared like the updraught in a gigantic flue. The top of a large wooden building a few yards from me suddenly burst upwards and every piece of loose wood was torn out. The top of a large corn stack and a straw stack nearby were whipped up into the air sheaf by sheaf as by a giant juggler, and held there before being flung aside. Heavy stone ridge-tiles were plucked from the house and the whole yard was full of flying stones and rubble as the disturbance passed over, leaving the air as quiet as before . . .

'My last general impression of the tornado as it moved away . . . was that it resembled, with its crashing uproar and smoke, a concentrated, creeping artillery barrage, moving away along a path about 60 yards wide.'

The tornado owes its origins, according to an article in the Royal Meteorological Society's eminent *Weather* magazine to the 'existence of a genesis of a minor front . . . with the convergence in the middle levels of two slow-moving markedly unstable air masses'. It is suggested that the atmospheric conditions were exacerbated by heat and moisture updraughting from two blast furnaces and a cooling tower at Clay Cross . . . 'Either of these features' concludes the article, 'could have provided an exceptionally vigorous air current to act as a trigger initiating a violent vortex.'

1st July 1952: The Kingsway Meteorite

'Is it a bird? Is it a plane? Is it a meteorite?' queried numerous residents of the Kingsway Estate in Derby. At the height of a furious storm in the city, many people believed they had heard the roar of a celestial visitor as it struck the ground. When the rains abated, a knot of curious astronomers gathered.

Sure enough, a missile had landed and it was hot and smoking. Measuring nine ft across and estimated to weigh between two and three tons, the object had an undoubted celestial provenance so one man broke a bit off and took it home as a souvenir.

Washed and spruced up, it was afforded mantelpiece prominence. But it began to emit noxious vapours and its owner feared an alien plot to poison the planet. And then, alarmingly, it disintegrated into a white powder.

The hot meteorite turned out to be nothing more sinister than an outsize lump of builder's lime. Was there one red face?

9th March 1955: True Grit

Highway maintenance at the Snake Pass reached explosive heights in an unprecedented operation by Derbyshire Council to avert the danger of avalanche. Following prolonged blizzard conditions, thousands of tons of snow and ice accumulated on the hillsides threatening traffic on the vital Manchester to Sheffield route. The road was closed whilst about 200 pounds of gelignite was deployed by a team of demolition experts. A small but successful trial blast around 11 o'clock gave a green light and two hours later the main plunger was depressed with dramatic results. Assistant County Surveyor Mr H.M. Horrocks reported, 'It did very good work and I am quite pleased with the result. It exceeded my expectations. About one third of the snow was dealt with in this way and comparatively little of it was brought down on the road. For the most part it was broken up or crumbled on the cornice of snow, which at an angle of 30 to 40 degrees rose to a height of about 200 ft above the road. In some places the actual cornice was overhanging about three to five ft over the road.'

1956: Blame it on the Bomb

Constant downpours in the region during the normally sunny month of August – the wettest in places for over 30 years – fuelled the debate on nuclear bomb testing and its effect on the weather. In pubs and clubs and in local newspapers the arguments raged but eminent scientists were quick to allay all our fears.

At the distinguished Nobel Prize Convention in West Germany boffins were unanimous in declaring that testing was not to blame for adverse weather conditions. 'People should stop getting wrought up about these explosions' reassured Professor Heinsenberg of Munich. 'It is possible that proof can be furnished in the presence of radioactive particles in rain, but they do not suffice to do any damage whatsoever. For the rest, my appetite would not suffer eating cauliflower drenched by radioactive rain.'

Thirty years later on the 26th April 1986 there was the near doomsday explosion at Chernobyl. Carried on prevailing wind, a radioactive cloud contaminated half of Europe, some of the deadly material being washed to earth in raindrops, polluting much of England and Scotland. Following tests, the National Radiological Protection Board admitted that contaminants in some ground samples constituted a significant risk. Milk production at several upland farms was constantly monitored and some farmers were banned from sending their carcasses to market although cauliflower sales were unaffected.

11th February 1957: The Big 'Quake

One of the most distinct earth tremors ever recorded in England sent afternoon shock waves across eleven English counties, causing damage and panic in towns as far apart as Blackpool and

Bristol. Being comparatively near to the computed epicentre of the tremor, in the Charnwood Forest area of Leicester, Nottinghamshire and Derbyshire were both badly shaken.

Some 10,000 square miles of the Midlands were affected, hundreds of chimney stacks across the twin counties crashing to the ground. Several people were hurt but there were many amazing escapes, particularly in Derby where the fire brigade received over 100 calls after damage to property. For a time St James's Street in Derby city centre was closed, structural damage to a shop creating a danger to traffic. Close by at Chaddesden a four year old boy was badly injured by a dislodged chimney pot. Nottingham centre was also severely jarred, even the castle feeling the shock. 'It seemed for a moment as if Castle Rock was disintegrating' said a passer-by. There were disturbing scenes in a Nottingham cinema. Half-way through the matinée, the floor, seats and screen began to vibrate violently and there was a mass stampede, men elbowing women aside in a panic to reach the emergency exits. Local builders were just washing down their trowels, when it happened again!

The second tremor struck just before midnight on the 12th February. 'It seemed to be worse than Monday's' said an alarmed resident of the YMCA in Nottingham. 'I lay in bed and felt several slight nudges at about 11.50 pm' reported N.R. Clarke of Riddall Road, Sherwood, Nottingham. '. . . no rock 'n' roll this time, definitely a shudder, there was a wind and a heavy rumble. The house shook and all the windows rattled.' The tremor was 'felt as a roar' in West Bridgford and damage was reported in Ilkeston, Borrowash, Stapleford and in Clifton where G. Gethem of Whitegate Vale had to remove fallen debris and smash open his front door to get to work. The fire brigade attended 21 dangerous buildings in Derby and there were a number of emergency calls from Long Eaton.

25th April 1957: Diesel Train Hit By Driftwood

Approaching Belper Station, the 7.27 train from Derby to Manchester was struck by a floating wooden manhole cover. The impact fractured the vacuum brake pipe and the diesel engine was stranded in mounting flood water for over three hours.

Elsewhere, storms filled watercourses to overflowing. Derby city centre was described by a council official as being 'completely under water'. In the town, Mansfield Road near the Derwent Hospital was smashed to pieces by pressure of underground water. Well known drapers Thurman and Malin of St Peter's Street had three pumps in action all day. Much of Duffield was inundated, the A6 trunk road was made impassable and about 160 Sandiacre families had to be rescued by lorries after the Erewash swirled into their homes.

1959: 'Proper Parched'

The loofahed tongue is symbolic of a year only eclipsed by 1976 in the annals of Derbyshire drought stretching back over 100 years. It was consistently hot, and the summer was exceptionally long. September saw only one day of rain and on the 3rd October the temperature in Belper reached 79°F. Beer and soft drink sales soared dramatically and there was a profligate use of water, so much so that the stocks in the massive Ladybower Reservoir shrank alarmingly. One local farmer took advantage of the retreating waters to visit the site of a family farm he had worked on 16 years earlier. He removed stones from the old farmstead to create a memorial rockery in Ashbourne in memory of his ancestral home flooded by the impounding of the Derwent.

Across the region, hosepipe bans were commonplace and standpipes were installed in a number of locations. The tinder

Drought conditions at Ladybower reservoir, 1959. (Sheffield City Libraries)

dry conditions on the moorlands heightened the threat of flash fires and there were a number of blazes.

Snippets from the Fifties

1952: The worst storm in living memory struck Derby and parts of Derbyshire on 1st June. Torrential rain, lightning strikes and falling trees and masonry left a trail of destruction.

1953: In one of Britain's worst ever disasters on the 31st January, some 300 people were killed in east coast storms. The popular Midlands holiday resort of Skegness was hit hard.

On the 3rd June, snow fell on the High Peak as Queen Elizabeth II was being crowned in Westminster Abbey.

1955: Unseasonal snows on the 17th May killed new-born lambs and blocked several roads in the Peak District.

1956: Forward thinking Derbyshire Council took delivery of a Swiss rotary snow-plough for testing during the winter months. It was an inspired purchase. The heaviest snowfalls for 50 years blanketed the region and on the 27th December all main roads in the Peak District around Buxton were blocked by drifts.

1957: The aerial spectacle of the aurora borealis was enjoyed in Nottinghamshire. 'It was one of the most brilliant displays of the northern lights I can ever remember,' said a Wollaton Park resident.

A Derbyshire record of 2.79 inches of rain fell on Gresley on the 6th July; 2.20 inches were reported in 40 minutes at Baslow. The 5th of August bank holiday at Rodsley was ruined after a storm deposited nearly six inches of rain.

Umbrellas again saw unprecedented service during September in Nottingham. An all time city record for September of 4.945 inches of rain caused the river Leen to overflow in Lenton. The accolade of England's lowest temperature for 1957 fell to Nottinghamshire's South Bonnington with − 16.1°C.

1958: The landmark windmill at North Leverton, Nottinghamshire was struck by lightning for the third time in its history. Damage was considerable. All four sails had to be replaced.

1959: In this exceptionally dry year, sunny accolades were awarded to Derby and Morley with 1517.9 hours and 1583.9 hours of the bright stuff respectively.

THE WEATHER IN
THE SIXTIES

30th May 1960: A Nottingham Whirlwind

A freak whirlwind which baffled the experts at the Watnall Weather Centre struck the Lenton district of Nottingham just after 2 o'clock on an otherwise still and balmy afternoon. The spiralling gust rattled windows throughout the district, crashed open doors and lifted a cricket sight screen into the air. An eye-witness, Nottingham city councillor Stanley Shelton of Gregory Street, Lenton, described the action. '. . . I was startled by a roar as my back door crashed open. Looking out of my window on to the sports ground I was amazed to see a cricket sight screen jump into the air and do a little dance. It stands on four iron wheels and weighs at least a ton.' Ernest Hill, groundsman at the Co-operative Society sports ground, who was in danger of being bowled over by the blast said, 'It was a terrible experience. It started as a shriek in the distance and got louder and louder. I thought for a second or two I was to be the first man lifted into space. I don't want another sensation like it . . . It was one of the worst moments of my life.'

10th December 1961: Slush and Bust

The worst December snowfalls in over 50 years left Christmas shoppers in Derby and Nottingham wading through ankle deep slush. Eight inches of overnight snow caused traffic chaos in both counties and gritters and snow-ploughs were hard pressed to keep routes open.

Conditions in Mansfield were described as treacherous and around Sutton-in-Ashfield there were huge drifts blocking a number of roads. Further west it was a similar story, residents of Alfreton and Ripley comparing conditions to those of 1947. Hundreds of householders had to cope with the misery of burst pipes, and power failures in Ripley blacked out local shops and the telephone exchange.

1963: Ice Age

In a New Year blast nearly the whole of Britain was covered in snow, an icy prelude to a year that left at least 49 people dead in bone chilling temperatures. The intensely low temperatures affected most of Europe. The river Danube froze for the first time in living memory, the Neptune fountain in Florence iced up and in Greece, hunger crazed wolves attacked villagers.

The new year weather was trumpeted in banner headlines – 'Blizzard Blitz on Derbyshire' declared the *Derby Telegraph* on the 3rd January, describing the efforts of 400 snow-plough crews in battles with the drifts. 'Blitz By Blizzard' heralded the *Nottingham Guardian Journal* comparing conditions to those of 1947. But the worst was yet to come.

By the 20th January, Britain had almost been 'cut in half' by blizzards, the heaviest snowfall since 1947 paralysing the entire Midlands. The river Derwent froze at Milford Bridge and eight

Walking on water. The frozen river Derwent, 25th January 1963. (Derby Evening Telegraph)

ft deep drifts closed many roads. The Matlock-Buxton road was blocked near Topley Pike where two coachloads of trippers were stranded on a return journey from a theatre in Manchester. The passengers spent the night huddled together for warmth before police broke through and escorted the party to the Waterloo Hotel in Taddington. The coach got stuck again two miles from the hotel and the journey had to be completed on foot.

A delivery driver with the Nottingham flour milling firm of Gilliatt and Sons has his own vivid recollections of that foul day. 'On this particular day, my mate and I had deliveries to make in the Melton Mowbray area, mostly down winding lanes and gated tracks . . . but we were defeated by the elements. We were battling against a real blizzard. The gale force wind was lashing into our faces and the sleet or ice was blasting more or less horizontally across the open fields . . . it was so severe that it drew blood on my partner's face.'

Veteran Barton bus driver and conductor George Sheard has another tale to tell about the 20th January. 'I set out with my driver to get to Cotgrave about eight miles south of Nottingham . . . but on arrival, no one dare travel. The snow was up to ten ft deep with 20 ft drifts. Eventually, two women came on the bus to do the shopping for all, because the village store owned by a Mr Wright had run out of food. We proceeded towards Nottingham via Holme House and Ratcliffe Road as we had been told that the road had been cleared, which was false. After a quarter of a mile, we skidded into a drift and were completely covered. The driver had bumped his head and was in danger. The two women were screaming and Fred and I got them out of the bus and they struggled back best they could. In the meantime, the hostler from Cotgrave Place Farm was coming towards us with two shire horses. Seeing our plight he fastened the horses to the bus with tractor chains and the bus (seven tons) was pulled onto the road and safety. We all went to the farm and Mr James the owner made us hot tea, whisky and toast. The two horses were rubbed down and got an extra treat in the stable.'

On the 21st January, the mothballed railway line between Buxton and Ashbourne was re-opened to bring relief to stranded villagers along the route. An engine fitted with a snow-plough buffeted the ten ft deep drifts. Villagers were told that the train would halt if hailed! But conditions worsened. The following day a mercy train left Buxton bound for Hartington. It floundered in deep drifts after only seven miles and was abandoned at Hindlow. But the weather was not all bad. It assisted police enquiries into a burglary at a Cotmanham store. The robbers had hoped to cover their tracks by dropping a stolen safe into the canal at Cossall. They reckoned without the ice!

Blizzards queued up to deposit their snow. A Derbyshire County Council spokesman lamented, 'Our men are working all out to clear the roads, but as fast as the snow is cleared the winds and blizzards sweep back again and it is a constant battle to keep stretches free.'

Moles, rabbits and miners are usually immune to such conditions. Not so Derbyshire coal workers. In some pits, six ft long icicles hung from underground shafts. NUM Secretary Bert Wynn explained. 'These icicles have stopped men going down shafts to do repair work for fear that scaffolding will disturb the ice and send it crashing down on the heads of those below. We are trying to alleviate the problem with braziers.'

Avoidable accidents were all too common. Blocked flues were blamed for a number of gas fire poisonings, there were several tragic deaths from hypothermia in the region and the Sherwood Foresters announced the demise of Private Derby, the regimental mascot. 'Derby was a victim of the cold weather,' said a spokesman. Road accidents were legion and there were a number of incidents on the railways. Icicles stopped an express train en route from Derby to Newcastle on the 25th January. As the engine entered a tunnel at Clay Cross, overhanging icicles struck the driver who was injured and taken to hospital.

A sudden thaw accounted for 500 burst pipes in homes on Nottingham's Bilborough Estate, but snow returned on the 30th January when avalanches threatened the Snake Pass. On the 3rd February police ordered the pass to be closed, the weather hampering efforts to blast it open with gelignite.

The 5th February: a venomous volley of blizzards, gales, rain and violent seas battered Britain. The High Peak villages of Aldwark, Hurdlow Town, Booth, Stoop and Brandside were all cut off as high winds whipped the snow into huge drifts. The problems multiplied. Power cuts to homes and industry were widespread and lay-offs in the building trades were inumerable. Sport also suffered, one FA Cup day alone losing 23 of the scheduled 32 games. Occupiers of homes with back boilers will remember the conditions well, the plight of Mrs Eileen Harrison of 25 Inglewood Road, Clifton Estate, Nottingham, being typical. As a consequence of frozen pipes, this poor widow was without a fire for two weeks and she was driven to spending half her weekly income on electricity and paraffin. 'It's an awful problem' said E.W.S. Martain of Nottingham Corporation. 'Our men have been working during weekends and putting in overtime every night to unfreeze houses but we still have a backlog.'

One unexpected consolation of the raw conditions could be discovered at local fishmongers. According to trawlermen, the Continental freeze, which had stopped all traffic on the Rhine, had encouraged vast shoals of sole to swim to warmer waters off the east coast of England, where they were gratefully caught for the English market. The finny abundance led to cheap prices.

The climatological excesses of 1963 were thought by many to have been worse than those of 1947 but they were certainly not as drawn out. According to records, temperatures in some parts of the region were the lowest since 1814 but at the end of February, the snow began to melt and on the 5th March, much milder air signalled the end of yet another eventful winter.

14th March 1964: The Four Inns Walk Tragedy

March can be a cruel month: season of burgeoning life – season of frosts and premature death. One of the worst tragedies ever to afflict the scouting movement came in the otherwise uneventful March of 1964 during the popular Four Inns Walk. In that fateful month, three young competitors died in appalling weather, early rain on the 14th turning malevolently to snow whipped up by a searching wind.

Almost 450 Rover Scouts set out in high spirits from the starting point near Holmfirth. The leading group of hikers crossed Bleaklow and Kinder Scout in rain and happily marched on to the Sunday finish unaware of the tragedy unfolding behind them. The temperature dropped, the rain turned to snow and within a

Crown Square ferry, Matlock, 11th December 1965. (Derby Evening Telegraph)

few minutes a blizzard raged. Check point controllers soon confirmed that four hikers were missing.

Two bedraggled souls were quickly located although one was so badly chilled that he died soon afterwards in hospital. Rescue teams searched frantically until dusk. The search was resumed on Monday at daybreak and one body was found in deep snow near a waterfall on the river Alport. The third victim was located the next day on open moorland above the Snake Pass. Tragically, the boy had been only ten minutes' hiking distance from safety.

18th July 1968: Pig Causes Flood

Brimful after 24 hours of incessant rain, the river Maun in Mansfield burst its banks, seriously flooding Bridge Street and

Derby street in flood, 10th December 1965. (Derby Evening Telegraph)

Church Street and bringing ruination to shops, houses and licensed premises. Surging through the thoroughfares without warning, the floodwaters gushed through doorways before preventative action could be taken and there was great consternation among traders when a passing bus created a bow wave that smashed one shop window, damaged another and left customers in the Bridge Tavern marooned. For a time, traffic was diverted around the town to allow the waters to subside and the work of boarding up and removal of sludge and slime to be completed.

Recriminations on the cause of the inundation continued for many weeks, irate shopkeepers blaming the local authority for installing a safety grill which, it was claimed, impeded the flow of the river. Harry Martin of Rock Court affirmed 'There's even a dead pig stuck behind it'.

26th August 1968: Lightning Misconduct

A television aerial acted as a lightning conductor to blast through the roof of a house in Littleover, Derbyshire, during a localised storm. For 45 minutes, torrential rain and hailstones peppered Number 76 Elms Avenue, where Mr A. Boyce was having a late meal.

'Suddenly there was a terrific explosion,' said Mr Boyce, 'and a blue light appeared in the fireplace. Soot, mortar and dust showered into the room – past my wife who was in the path of the blast. Fortunately she was not hurt.'

The lightning badly damaged the chimney stack, punched a three ft wide hole in roofing slates, burnt out various electrical connections and short circuited the mains supply.

February 1969: Kind of Cool

The High Peak area of Derbyshire enjoys a somewhat different climate to the rest of the county. Skegness has long had a motto about the bracing airs of its fair town . . . but compared to this!

Spy a single snow flake at sea level – grab the goggles to contest a blizzard in this fair place – a place apart.

The roads in this elevated windswept country are perennially subject to closure, hardly a winter going by without some blockage or disruption. Residents hereabouts, people and their hardy flocks of sheep, have to be resilient and prepared for the worst like the Gee family of Hill House, Kinder.

A stupendous February 1969 blizzard is part of the Gee family legend. Consulting her diary, Pam Gee recounts the tale. 'On the morning of the 20th February, my husband was up early, woken

Above and over page: *Kinder cool... Snowdrifts at Kinder, Derbyshire, February 1969. (Mrs P Gee)*

by a raging wind. Drifts were swirling into fantastic shapes before our eyes and during that morning we watched helplessly as the snow gradually covered the car until it was completely buried under an enormous snow blanket. Arthur and I togged up to go to the Land Rover. It was like a nightmare – driving snow, a bleak wind and huge drifts. The milk was there so we sledged some up. The wind had kept blowing the front door open, filling the porch with snow.

89

'The following day the back of the house had a drift as high as the landing window and we had to dig, first a hole, then steps to get out of the back door. We began digging out the car and clearing buckets of snow from the loft; immensely hard work but in the brilliant sun, the scenery was from a fairy tale.'

March 1969: Glazed Expressions

Derbyshire residents contended with a severe easterly gale on the 19th February, coping with up to ten inches of snow deposited in just five hours. With spring bursting forth one month later they swapped their wellingtons for plimsolls unaware of a slippery menace above. Trapped under a blanket of cold air, water saturated clouds released their rain which became super cooled as it fell to earth, striking the ground as glaze and coating everything in a slippery film of ice, the involuntary triple salchows giving hilarious but dangerous expression to the colourful Derbyshire saying 'arse over apex'.

The glaze was particularly pronounced at higher levels. Weighed down by accumulated coatings of ice, the Independent Television Company's Emley Moor transmitter in Yorkshire, at an elevation of 1,270 ft, collapsed. At a similar height of 1,125 ft, the Fox House Inn and the nearby Longshaw Woods in northern Derbyshire were severely glazed. Ice of a remarkably consistent thickness of one inch completely covered the windward walls and the chimneys of the inn despite its being heated. A barn close by was also encased. Tree trunks in the woods sparkled in an icing sugar glaze up to two inches thick, the ice extending roughly 140 degrees around each bole, being thickest in the face of the prevailing wind. Many trees were damaged. The cemented crowns of Scots pine were particularly vulnerable – although many birches, because of their inherent elasticity under ice loading, survived intact. Overhead telephone lines and electricity supply cables were also brought down.

Sixties Summary

1960: In complete contrast to the dryness of the previous year, 1960 was exceptionally wet, particularly in Derbyshire where nearly 14 inches of rain fell during autumn. Only autumn 1935 was wetter since records were first compiled in 1880.

1962: In February, a vicious gale toppled a long revered landmark at Beauchief in the Peak District. One of a venerable pair of oaks, the centuries old tree came crashing to the ground.

1963: The newly published *British Atlas* awarded Nottingham the dubious title of Foggiest Town In Britain.

1965: On 12th May the temperature in Nottingham reached a UK high of 75°F.

December in the region was very wet. During the month, Belper recorded 7.44 inches of rain. The Derwent overflowed in Derby flooding the Chester Green district of the town.

A staggering total of 16.80 inches of rain fell at Featherbed Top in the High Peak area during December. The average yearly rainfall for the local weather station is 54 inches.

1966: The Nottinghamshire village of Wellow celebrated the erection of a replacement maypole in April following the loss of the previous pole in a gale.

1968: A storm in the Derby area on the 18th April ended a long period marked by the absence of heavy rain. The A6 at Duffield and the road at Littleover Hollow were flooded.

1969: March in Derbyshire was the coldest this century.

'Got any beef dripping?' A jolly Ashbourne butcher, December 1965.
(Derby Evening Telegraph)

THE WEATHER IN THE SEVENTIES

23 July 1972: A Trail of Destruction

Vanguard hailstones the size of marbles led an aerial assault which caused widespread damage and destruction throughout the two counties. Some localities recorded one inch of rain in only 20 minutes, hail drifts were over three ft deep in places and there was widespread flooding and transport dislocation. Roads in the Ashbourne area were swamped and at Cubley on the Derbyshire/Staffordshire boundary, an entire bridge was swept away. Farm crops were pulverised around Derby and further east, the A1 was closed to traffic at Newark. Elsewhere, manhole covers popped like corks.

In Nottingham city centre, the newly opened Victoria Centre car park flooded to a depth of three ft. Makeshift lifeboats were commandeered in the nearby Sherwood and Carrington districts to rescue drivers from submerged cars and the congregation in St Peter's church in the Radford area had an electrifying experience. The incumbent, the Revd J.S. Lemon, had just commenced reciting 'lighten our darkness' when there was a divine response and the roof caved in. A biblical flash tore away part of the roof, and undeflected, the cannonade of hailstones played a tune on the pock-marked piano. The 30 worshippers took refuge in the aisles. 'As we sheltered' explained the vicar 'one of the congregation remarked that all we needed was an ark. Hail was eight inches deep . . . '

2nd June 1975: It's Not Cricket

An invasion by aliens would have had less impact on the second day of play at Buxton between Derbyshire and Lancashire. A snowstorm soon after midday quickly covered the whole playing area in a white mantle. 'I've never seen owt like it,' said Yorkshire umpire 'Dicky' Bird. Heavy snow also interrupted the game between Essex and Kent in Colchester.

3rd January 1976: Killer Gale

Hurricane force winds gusting up to 90 mph caused extensive damage throughout Derbyshire. A toppled tree fell on a house in Hazelwood and killed the occupant and uprooted trees and debris blocked many roads. Power and telephone lines were brought down and there were scores of injuries. Derbyshire Royal Infirmary treated more than 40 people for cuts and bruises and the emergency services answered around 1,200 calls in less than 18 hours. The gable end of a block of flats was blown out in Staveley and at Mam Tor, three occupants of an upturned car were hurt.

1976: A Dried Out Piece of Sacking

A stark headline described the effects of the worst drought in England since 1720, the relentless sunshine fuelling a fierce and continuing debate about global warming, fossil fuel emissions, ozone depletion, rain forest exploitation and our profligate use of water. For congenitally welly-booted Brits, the absence of murk was the clearest argument yet for conservation.

Flood water in overfilled sewers bursting through the roadway, Church Street, Mansfield, July 1973. (Chad-Mansfield Chronicle Advertiser)

Mansfield's worst flooding in 60 years, completely submerged the town centre. Scene here of Bridge Street, Church Street and Toothill Lane junction, 24th July 1972. (Chad – Mansfield Chronicle Advertiser)

Another view of Bridge Street outside the Bridge Tavern. The car was swept 100 yards by the torrent of water, 24th July 1972. (Chad – Mansfield Chronicle Advertiser)

Gale fatality at Hazelwood. An elderly man was killed when a giant tree smashed into his bedroom, 3rd January 1976. (Derby Evening Telegraph)

Giant hailstones at Mickleover, Derby, 1976. (Derby Evening Telegraph)

Water stocks were already low in reservoirs when the drought set in in June, July and August recording almost endless sunshine and record temperatures. June in Chesterfield was awarded the accolade of 'hottest since 1659'. On 25th June, Centre Court temperatures at Wimbledon reached 106°F. There was a run on ice cream, soft drinks and beer – over indulgent sunbathers caused unprecedented sales of calamine lotion! It was heat all the way. Thousands of people across the region discarded pyjamas and nightdresses in an attempt to keep cool but sleep was a sweaty dream as temperatures nudged 60°F even in the early morning.

Sun worshippers were out in earnest, large numbers flocking to bathe in the Trent and the Derwent and to picnic in parks and public places. On the 3rd July in Debenhams' Derby store over 100 children's paddling pools were sold, the store director reassuring water conservationists with some well chosen words. 'Purchasers are finding ways of utilising the final rinsing water from their washing machines.'

For those in work, the heat was unbearable. Indoors, the mercury almost burst its glass and hundreds of workers walked out in protest. Foundries and heavy engineering plants were worst affected but poorly ventilated shops also swooned in the cauldron heat, the temperature in Derby's Eagle Centre in early July reaching a staggering 120°F.

The alarming rate of water consumption and the tinder dry condition of woods and moorlands were the main problems. Hosepipe bans had wide application across the region, stand pipes were readied and Sherwood Forest was closed to the public to reduce the risk of fire.

During August there was an exceptional dry spell. Between 31st July and 27th August, not a single drop of rain fell at Borrowash near Derby and there were similar reports from other weather

99

stations in the region. In a bid to save water the famous fountain at Chatsworth House near Bakewell was turned off and visitors to the Osberton Horse Trials near Worksop were warned to extinguish cigarettes in response to the danger of fire. Supplying water to most of the East Midlands, the Peak District reservoirs – Derwent, Ladybower and Howden – dwindled and dire warnings were given about the possibilities of the introduction of stand-pipes should the drought continue. Then up popped cantankerous September with a downpour. Everyone steamed and dug out their macs. Perversely enough, rainfall during February 1977 in some areas broke all records since 1880. Funny stuff this weather!

14th January 1977: The Long Walk Home

Thousands of commuters and pedestrians endured arduous journeys from the centre of Nottingham after a day of near-Arctic blizzards. The plight of one wretched soul who opted for the long walk home made the evening press . . . 'I hit the road (literally) an hour after setting off so blithely, a hermit-like figure who resembled an undernourished fur trapper emerging from the Saskatchewan tundra. Three buses, having prised themselves loose from the glaciers . . . rumbled past, loaded to the gills. Even with a spare seat I wouldn't have blamed any driver for ignoring the apparition who stood beckoning like the Ancient Mariner, coated a ghostly white and with a visor of icicles glinting in the headlights . . . for another three-quarters of an hour my journey through the wasteland ground on. My trousers froze, unfroze then froze again. I could hear the water squelching about in my socks like two retired hot water bottles. Then, one last bend and I was there. But as I tottered into the home stretch bruised and beyond repair my merry little children leapt out from behind the snowman they had built and, chortling with welcoming glee, pelted me with snowballs. I just didn't have the strength to kill them.'

Going for a spin in Hulland village, February 1979. (Mrs B Allsop)

A council spademan admires his handiwork, Hulland village, March 1979. (Mrs B Allsop)

While stocks last... Gary Draper at his Mapperley store, Westdale Lane, 28th January 1979. (Nottingham Evening Post)

1979: Winter Woe Land

Comparable in ferocity to the winter of 1947, the big freeze of 1979, characterised by biting cold and driving blizzards, brought dislocation and devastation across both counties. Conditions across Britain were dour, the problems becoming so acute that the government appointed the irrepressible Denis Howell as Minister for Snow.

Christmas 1978 temperatures in the region were comparatively mild but January 1979 began bitterly cold, the thermometer registering − 16°C at Markeaton Park, Derby. January was eventful in statistical terms, being the coldest month since 1963,

Eskimo style. The MacKay children at their home in Keyworth, Nottinghamshire, 20th February 1979. (Nottingham Evening Post)

but it was easily outdone by February – a month of blitzkrieg blizzards and blocked roads.

Comparisons with the Arctic were well founded on the 15th February when massive snowdrifts cut off scores of towns and villages. Eight major roads were blocked in Nottinghamshire and 25 in Derbyshire. The seriousness of the situation was succinctly put by a police spokesman, 'If you're travelling up the M1 you might not come back.' The treacherous roads caused horrendous driving conditions. Journeys into work were at snail's pace, there was widespread absenteeism and schools by the dozen closed. Some commuters improvised. A Juror at Derby Crown Court travelled in by tractor and one enterprising commuter was seen speeding down Westdale Lane, Mapperley, on skis. Rural communities, especially in the High Peak, endured terrible hardships. Sheep and cattle had to be rescued from deep snow. One farmer in Fairfield used a helicopter to ferry fodder to stranded stock. Whole fields of winter vegetables were ruined and, such was the intensity of the cold, that many holly trees and laurel bushes lost all their leaves. In Yorkshire, Operation Siberia swung into action to rescue embattled motorists on the M62.

The 15th was bad, but the 16th was worse. Caught in 15 ft drifts, abandoned cars and lorries littered routes throughout the two counties. Mansfield, Sutton-in-Ashfield and parts of Kirkby were reported by the AA to be completely cut off. Derbyshire was virtually at a standstill, motorists on high level routes having to seek shelter to avoid being buried alive.

Snow continued to fall until the end of February but the quantities diminished. The thaw came and with it a welter of car insurance claims and questions about the overspending of winter maintenance budgets.

Seventies Synopsis

1970: Heavy winter rains and persistent snow flurries helped fill the Ladybower, Derwent and Howden reservoirs to overspill capacity after mid-October 1970 levels of 35 ft below maximum.

1971: The mild winter was beneficial to trout stocks in Derbyshire rivers but after an extremely fine spell of weather in July and August, anglers were thwarted by a succession of violent storms. One drenched rod witnessed a deluge of 1.81 inches of rain in just 75 minutes. Rivers and streams overflowed, the diminutive Hamps near Ashbourne rose by 21 ft and caused great havoc to bankside residents, dozens of whom were evacuated from their homes. Much of the weed growth in the Dove was scoured out and the profile of its bed was considerably altered.

On the 20th March, a freak thunderbolt struck a Derbyshire farm. St Bride's Farm at Stanton-by-Bridge was hit by what one fireman described as 'the most powerful blast I have ever seen'. The strike inflicted massive structural damage and 20% of the contents of the farmhouse were wrecked. The attendant thunderclap was heard in Derby and Mickleover.

1972: Dry conditions persisted until autumn in Derbyshire. Some local rivers were reduced to mere trickles.

1973: The Nottinghamshire Weather Station in Watnall reported the mildest winter on record, noting a total of only eleven air frosts. February was exceptional for its absence of snow. March in Derbyshire was consistently sunny and dry.

1974: In drought conditions, 500 fish were rescued from de-oxygenated pools in the upper reaches of Derbyshire's river Lathkill and released further downstream.

Following an extremely cold snap in November, the Cocker Beck at Lowdham, Nottinghamshire froze solid. There were more bizarre happenings in the same locality a few weeks later. Unseasonally mild conditions caused a flush of growth on hawthorn trees and at midnight on 30th December a local resident reported a bird in song. 'It appeared confused by the springlike warmth and the orange sodium lights as it flitted from tree to tree.'

1975: Whirlwinds were reported in Nottinghamshire during a period of thunder and heavy rain on the 12th January.

Aftermath of a ten minute storm, Meden Square, Pleasley Hill, Mansfield, 15th July 1975. Some of the hail stones were the size of pigeon's eggs and caused both tremendous damage and flooding. (Chad-Mansfield Chronicle Advertiser)

Novelty ices in the Water Lane area of Pleasley Hill, 15th July 1975. (Chad – Mansfield Chronicle Advertiser)

As a consequence of heavy rain on the 15th March, floodwaters cut off Whatton in South Nottinghamshire. Homes in Colston Bassett were inundated and carpets and furniture ruined.

Still reeling, five days after the appearance of snow in Derby, residents sweltered on the 7th June in a temperature of 82°F. The thermometer reached 90.9°F on the 8th August. Weather commentators in Nottingham warned 'whole areas of the countryside are virtual powder kegs'.

1976: Derbyshire's river Bradford retreated underground during an exceptional period of drought. From July to November much of its course was completely dry, many local inhabitants feared it had disappeared forever.

1977: The rainfall tally in the Chesterfield area in February was one of the highest on record – a total of 9.61 inches – a figure only surpassed by the totals for May 1886, August 1922 and November 1951.

On the 8th October, travelling north-north-west on a line east of Newark, a tornado roared through the Nottinghamshire countryside. No more than 50 ft wide it was described by a petrified onlooker as 'like a very heavy lorry coming up the garden path'.

1978: The longest cold spell in some areas since 1963 was exacerbated in February by an overtime ban involving 600 Derbyshire road gritting workers.

1979: May Day dawned across Derbyshire revealing snow.

THE WEATHER IN
THE EIGHTIES

10th July 1981: Derby-on-Sea

Everything but the kitchen sink fell on Derby on that memorable Friday, the seaside comparisons prompted by barefoot pedestrians paddling in the rain. The wettest day in 40 years brought a monumental 3.15 inches of water cascading through the city streets, inundating shops and offices, stranding motorists, closing schools and causing a hurried evacuation of kidney patients at the Derby City Hospital. Local weather watcher Philip Singleton was caught in the storm.

'It was a dull, sticky day,' he recalls. 'After 2 pm it began to grow progressively darker. By 3.30 a dense wall of grey cloud could be seen reaching high into the sky and 15 minutes later the storm broke and lasted 75 minutes. It became so dark that automatic street lights were triggered and visibility was severely reduced by the intensity of the rain. Manhole covers were lifted by the force of the water and numerous roads were turned into rivers and lakes bringing traffic to a standstill as vehicles became stranded in the flood water. Those unfortunate to be caught in the open were instantly drenched. Numerous business premises were flooded and had to suspend business for the day. After the storm, many large boulders and soil could be seen littering the pavements – a testimony to the ferocity of the water.'

GET ON TWO WHEELS SAMWAYS
MOTOR BIKES — BIKES
121 Nuns St., — 70A Friar Gate,
Derby — Derby
Tel: 46456 — Tel: 366640

DERBY

Evening Telegraph

Butlers
Office Equipment for
PHILIPS WORD
PROCESSING
Tel: Derby 40571
for details

No. 31,165 — FRIDAY, JULY 10, 1981 — 10p

CITY SWAMPED

CITY TRAFFIC ploughs through the flooded inner ring road in Eastgate. BELOW: This young woman goes barefoot in the rain.

WE WERE HIT, TOO

LIKE so many other buildings in Derby yesterday the Evening Telegraph premises at Meadow Road were affected by the downpour and through this and road congestion and flooding the dispatch of newspapers was disrupted.

Remedial operations continue, but because of the effect of the storm we regret that we are unable to publish as normal today.

Lifelines in one-day gas strike

EMERGENCY services will be maintained during the one-day strike which has been called by gas unions for Monday.

The unions have promised emergency cover during the period of the industrial action which has been called in protest against the Government's plan to dispose of gas showrooms.

Although normal installation or maintenance jobs will not be done on Monday, in the event of a suspected gas escape the number listed under GAS in all telephone directories, say Emgas.

They are apologised to customers for whom work was planned on Monday and say that new appointments will be made as soon as possible.

Firemen overcome by fumes

THREE firemen were in hospital today, two of them very seriously ill, after being overcome by carbon monoxide fumes in a North London basement.

The firemen were pumping out a flooded basement in Wood Green High Road when they collapsed.

All three were taken to North Middlesex Hospital.

3-in of rain falls in 70 minutes

HOMES, shops, factories and roads were swamped yesterday afternoon as Derby was hit by its worst storm for more than 30 years.

Emergency services worked flat out to deal with problems caused by the freak downpour. More than 3-in of rain fell in 70 minutes.

Four schools were so badly flooded that pupils were given the day off today as mopping up operations continued.

The storm, caused by rocketing humidity and temperatures, centred on the Derby and Ashbourne areas.

Other outlying centres such as Burton, Dawston and Ripley had the worst effects.

More than 1,000 homes were still without power in the Ashbourne area today because

of a lightning strike on an electricity supply box.

Kidney patients at Derby City Hospital were disconnected from kidney machines and evacuated from a ward as floodwater made treatment impossible.

Flooding also hit Derbyshire Royal Infirmary and the Manor Hospital but no patients had to be evacuated.

Traffic ground to a halt as up to 2ft of water covered parts of the Inner Ring Road in Derby.

A foot of water was running through the streets of Bakewell at the height of the storm.

More than 1,000 telephone subscribers were cut off and British Telecom engineers are working to clear lines.

Local firms were today counting the cost of storm damage as clearing up operations continued.

Storm pictures and reports —
pages 3, 6, 7, 25

Air death crash caused by door

THE CREW of the Dan-Air HS748 aircraft which crashed near East Midlands Airport two weeks ago lost control when a door flew off and smashed into the tailplane.

This had been established by Department of Trade accident investigators after a preliminary examination of the wreckage, the Commons heard yesterday.

The aircraft was carrying mail from Gatwick to Castle Donington.

Its crew of two and a Post Office mail assistant died when it dived steeply into the ground near the village of Eyre.

Meanwhile, the Civil Aviation Authority has rushed out a mandatory instruction to all HS748 operators, warning that strict checks must be

done on the locking mechanism of the door.

The "Preliminary examination of the aircraft wreckage showed the standard rear cabin service door had become detached in flight and had struck the starboard tailplane, leading to a loss of control and subsequent overstressing of the aircraft.

The reasons for the separation of the door have yet to be established," said Mr Eyre.

Knifepoint rape

Police were today seeking a man who raped a 36-year-old married woman who was walking her dogs on Hampshire — yesterday afternoon. The man, aged 25 - 30, was armed with a knife.

More steel

Steel production in Britain averaged 326,900 tonnes a week in June, the highest since the strike.

The June output was up per cent above the May figures, and 33.2 per cent above the average rate for the last six months of 1980.

Turn to Back Page

Stop Press. Front page of Derby Evening Telegraph, 10th July 1981. (Derby Evening Telegraph)

Bus crash at Radbourne Common near Kirk Langley, Derbyshire, 8th February 1983. (Derby Evening Telegraph)

1983: New Year Revolutions

The strains of Auld Lang Syne had barely died away when gales lashed the East Midlands, the term gyratory system taking on a whole new meaning as vehicles were spun like tops in 60 mph winds. Dozens of routes in Derbyshire were blocked by abandoned lorries and cars and by drifting snow. Scores of trees fell victim to the atrocious conditions, one 90 ft high poplar being lowered to safety by firemen at Mapperley to prevent damage to a cottage. Actual damage was widespread. In Nottingham, the Turney Street depot of the City Transport Department lost its plastic roof. In London, the gates of the newly installed Thames Barrier were lowered for the first time.

Not to be outdone, the opening day of spring in the region on 21st March was equally as bad, a mixture of snow, hail, sleet and rain causing long traffic delays. On the A628, the appalling weather led to a five mile tail-back as far as Glossop.

13th January 1984: Friday 13th Mayhem

Spawned by a vigorous depression centred on South Yorkshire, hurricane force winds and torrential rain brought chaos and a trail of destruction to northern parts of Derbyshire and Nottinghamshire. Gusts of over 90 mph coupled with blinding rain made driving extremely hazardous and many roads were blocked by fallen trees and toppled vehicles. Two lanes of the M1 at South Normanton were closed by upturned lorries and firemen rescued three people from a car crushed by a fallen tree on the Pleasey to Upper Langwith Road. Hundreds of Chesterfield residents suffered roof damage, the East Midlands Electricity Board was called upon to restore power after cables were torn down and there was widespread damage mostly to trees and chimney stacks in Buxton, although miraculously, no one was seriously hurt. Worksop and Retford town centres were also affected.

January 1984: Snow Go Slow

Three days of snow brought traffic chaos to the region. Exasperated drivers abandoned cars by the roadside, drifting snow blocked eight main roads in Derbyshire and city centre stores and offices closed early. Across both counties, telephone lines were brought down, schools were closed and market attendances were markedly down. On the 23rd January only two stallholders turned up at Nottingham Market out of a usual complement of over 100! There was a big demand for wellington boots in Wakefield's Lister Gate shop in the town. 'We've sold so many we've lost count,' said an assistant.

21st January 1987: A Whiter Shade of Pail

On the 12th January, blizzards swept the north of England. On that bitterly cold day, temperatures in some places never rose above freezing and there was widespread chaos on the roads. Subsequent snow storms closed schools, disrupted industrial production and led to the mass abandonment of over 1,000 vehicles on the Trans-Pennine motorway (M62).

By the 21st January, the situation in some elevated parts of Derbyshire became desperate. Dozens of isolated hamlets were cut off by deep drifts. The persistently low temperatures caused water pipes to freeze, even underground mains becoming rock solid. Embattled farmers Carol and Ralf Burton of Old House Farm, Dove Holes near Buxton, remember the conditions well.

Ice cream cornice. Swarkestone, Derbyshire, February 1984. (Mr B J Sims)

Mrs Celia Kelly surveys a culprit tree toppled by a gale, 23rd September 1988. (Derby Evening Telegraph)

'All the cows were inside and so had no water. The milk cows were let out to a brook which runs round the farm. The young cattle would have gone mad if we had let them out so we had to go to the brook with buckets and milk churns and fill them with water and carry them up to the yard for the cows . . . Eventually, after having no water for several days we managed to thaw out the mains pipe. Then the fun started. All the water pipes in the parlour burst . . . then we had more than enough water!'

16th October 1987: The Mother of All Storms

Calmed by the bedtime assurances of Michael Fish, the nation slept soundly, confident in the knowledge that weather ships, satellites, banks of sophisticated computers and posses of meteorological boffins were keeping a watchful eye. But everything was on the blink! Unbeknown to these observers, a massive storm was brewing out in the English Channel. Suddenly it changed track and an explosive depression roared in from the south-west and hit southern England in the early hours of the morning. Winds well in excess of 100 mph demolished hundreds of homes and factories and public buildings, smashed cars and boats to smithereens and left scores of people dead. Communications were crippled and millions of trees were uprooted, the swathe of destruction changing the topography of several counties.

Nottinghamshire and Derbyshire escaped the winds although the eye of the storm passed close to the region. Gusts of 60 mph were recorded and there was some damage, although compared to that of southern counties, this was slight.

Eighties Dribs and Drabs

1980: On the 15th January, unprecedented chaos on Nottingham's snow and ice covered roads was blamed on panic-stricken motorists. Many drivers abandoned their cars and blocked roads led to almost total paralysis.

1981: Topsy-turvy weather in the Peak District brought April temperatures of 68°F and 20 inch snow falls. All roads in the area were closed at midday on the 25th.

A fireball blasted the chimney stack of an Ashbourne home on the 20th May, severely damaging the roof. 'There was a great red ball to the west with sheets of flame shooting out of it' said an eyewitness.

Hot rods at Victoria Embankment, Nottingham, 4th May 1989. (Nottingham Evening Post)

A blizzard swept through the region on the 13th December, gale force winds piling snow into five ft deep drifts. Many minor roads were blocked across the two counties, cutting access to scores of towns and villages.

1982: In 48 hours between the 21st and 22nd of June, Chesterfield had 4.3 inches of rain. In that soggy month, some weather stations in the region reported up to three times the normal rainfall.

1983: Purple lightning was observed during a severe thunderstorm in Matlock on the 22nd April. At Cromford there was structural damage to property, lightning struck a house in Birchover and a whirlwind demolished a haybarn at Wirksworth

Moor Farm. On the same day there was torrential rain and flash flooding in Nottinghamshire. The village of Oxton was cut off by deep water and mud.

On the 22nd August 'dust devils' were reported at Bleasby near Newark. The observer described a vigorously shaken hedge, and straw and dust whirled into the sky by a vortex of spiralling air about two to three metres wide.

1984: A tornado swept through Gotham, Nottinghamshire on the 2nd August.

1985: The 'Indian summer' reached its peak on the 1st October when some parts of the region basked in the warmest temperatures of the year. Newark enjoyed 28.6°C, Carlton 28.0°C and in Nottingham it was the hottest October day since at least 1840!

1986: Heavy snow and freezing temperatures led to a spate of vehicle collisions on the 6th February. Skid-pan road conditions caused 75 crashes in Nottinghamshire alone. Snow-ploughs battled to keep routes open in Derbyshire where the bad weather brought down power lines and plunged 1400 homes into darkness.

National weather forecasters were berated on the 12th February for failing to predict the onset of freezing temperatures and blizzards. In a four-day period, the Queens Medical Centre at Nottingham treated 472 more winter accident casualties than normal.

Lightning struck a house in Stretton on the 20th May, slightly injuring the occupant. There was flash flooding in Derby and Darley Abbey suffered significant damage.

1987: Dubbed 'Black Friday' the 17th July was an unlucky day for many localities in the Nottingham area. Afternoon storms brought power cuts and flash flooding. Farnsfield village was awash and the Dunkirk, Lenton and West Bridgford districts were badly affected.

1988: Heavy snowfalls on the 22nd January made driving conditions in south Nottinghamshire extremely hazardous. Some hills round Arnold and Gedling were impassable. Telephone lines were brought down at Bilborough and the East Midlands airport was closed.

Whirlwinds near the Derbyshire/Staffordshire border on the 26th July split and felled trees. Two cows were killed by falling boughs and bushes were observed blowing in a circular motion.

November snows in Derbyshire were the earliest in that month for 16 years.

1989: The aurora borealis was seen across the region on the 13th March.

INTO THE NINETIES

25th January 1990: It Happened Again!

According to meteorological statistics, storms like the mind blowing corker of the 16th October 1987 visit England every 250 years. So less than three years on, the big blow of 1990 was in these terms at least unexpected! It differed from its predecessor in three notable respects. Firstly, it arrived during daylight hours, striking a country on the move. Secondly, chastened weather forecasters gave us some time in which to batten down the hatches. And thirdly, and most importantly as far as this region was concerned, it tracked north.

'Gusts here were of hurricane force' said Jim Gould of the Watnall Weather Centre. The M1 was littered with toppled vehicles and the northbound carriageway was closed by the police for four hours. One driver of an upturned articulated lorry managed to radio for help as he hung upside down in his cab. Another driver suffered whiplash injuries sustained when a fallen tree smashed into her car at Forest Town near Mansfield. Power lines were brought down, over 20,000 homes around Mansfield and Nottingham losing electricity supplies. In Derbyshire, police recorded 193 uprooted trees and 19 vehicles overturned. Minor damage to roofs, fences, greenhouses and sheds was extensive and as the winds died down insurance holders spent hours poring over small print.

Early January snows in 1990 brought down power lines at Farnsfield near Mansfield. Here, linesmen repair the damage. (Mansfield Chronicle Advertiser)

The national insurance cost of the storm, when totalled with that for gale damage sustained in February 1990, was reckoned to be in the region of £2,081 million compared with the £1,227 bill for the hurricane of 1987.

1990: Daffodils in February

The first year of the Nineties was notable for its warmth. The winter months proved to be very mild and spring flowers blossomed in mid-February, making the season the warmest in Derbyshire since 1945 and the driest since 1938. During a very hot August the temperature in Chaddesden reached 96°F, the highest recorded reading in Derbyshire this century. The year was not without inclemencies, however. On the 8th December a

The A38 near Fullwood was closed after severe blizzards, January 1990. Many vehicles were abandoned in the drifts. (Chad-Mansfield Chronicle Advertiser)

damaging snowstorm in Derbyshire encased power cables in ice. They snapped under the weight, crashing to the ground and dislocating telephone communications and electricity supplies. And in Nottinghamshire on the 10th December emergency services were at full stretch coping with a crop of accidents caused by heavy snow. Such were the terrible road conditions that one ambulanceman had to walk from Lambley to Arnold to assist a patient.

1992: Quick Flashes and Crashes

Between the 8th and 9th August, several thunderstorms targeted the twin counties. The storms were characterised by the frequencies of thunderclaps and strikes of lightning. At

Keyworth in Nottinghamshire up to 30 lightning flashes per minute were recorded and actual lightning strikes were frequent. A house in Carlton was struck and set ablaze and there were widespread power cuts in settlements along the Nottinghamshire/Leicestershire boundary.

In a rush of Christmas blood to the head, irresponsible drivers on the M1 were involved in a 30 vehicle pile-up at junction 30 near Chesterfield in sub-zero temperatures and thick fog. Part of the road was closed for the second time in three days, the previous accidents having claimed three lives. Derbyshire Assistant Chief Constable Don Dovaston said, 'People seem to have a total disregard for the safety of themselves and other road users. These drivers are selfish and some of the driving we have witnessed was beyond belief. Motorists are doing 70 mph in dreadful conditions when you can barely see in front of your nose.' In one incident a speeding lorry ran over a police car!

1993: A Changeable Climate

All known varieties of the inimitable British weather graced the twin counties in this year of meteorological mediocrity. It rained, it poured, there were floods, gales and blizzards and sub-zero temperatures all capped by a miserable summer that turned gardens into paddy fields and neighbours green with envy for the chaps next door who had booked a fortnight in Marbella!

Torrential rain lashed the region on the 13th September. A depressing autumn faded into a dreary winter and by late November chill winds sent temperatures plummeting. 'The origin of all this is Russia,' explained a long-range forecaster. 'A record temperature of − 54.6°C was reached in eastern Siberia and is now blowing its way across from the east.' British Rail girded its loins for the possibility of worsening weather. 'We learned a lot of lessons from the now-famous wrong type of snow

121

fall,' said a spokesman. 'It was no joke. It was a different type of snow than we normally experience – it was powdery. We now have a number of measures guarding the air intakes on locomotives to protect the engines.' These measures were tested on the 22nd November when the whole of eastern England awoke to deep snow.

On the unlucky Friday 13th December, 13 people died as freak gales swept across Britain. Many houses in the region sustained damage. At sea, the Royal Navy destroyer HMS *Nottingham* joined in a fruitless search for a sailor washed overboard from a Dutch fishing vessel.

Blizzards on the 13th December closed a number of roads in Derbyshire and one week later came another deluge, followed by further snow and sleet on the 21st. The year ended with yet more snow. Six inches fell in the Peak District on 29th December blocking dozens of roads and cutting off a number of villages. In Nottinghamshire, the A57 near Worksop was closed and only a single lane of the M1 remained open. Football matches at the Notts County and Mansfield grounds were postponed, but the East Midlands derby between Derby and Leicester went ahead.

1994: Annus Horribilis

The start of 1994 was nothing to write home to the Queen Mother about. Torrential rain continued to lash England after a soggy December – the wettest month of 1993. The Cornish fishing village of Polperro mopped up and assessed a £1 million flood repair bill and a yellow alert was announced by the National Rivers Authority for the stretch of the lower Trent between Newark and Gainsborough. On the 10th January, 100 soldiers from the 36th Royal Engineers began erecting two pontoon bridges in an attempt to maintain access to the water-besieged city of Chichester.

February brought blizzards, more rain and gales. On the 2nd February all trans-Pennine routes were closed for a time by heavy snow and the wind proved troublesome at Windy Harbour, Derbyshire where a van was blown over twice within a few minutes by 60 mph gusts. Strong winds and heavy rain were blamed for snapping overhead cables and bringing chaos to railway timetables in the Newark and Retford areas. And the region shivered on Shrove Tuesday, blizzards and high winds causing a number of accidents on the A1 in North Nottinghamshire. Mid-February and snow again brought treacherous conditions on the roads. The A1 near Newark was badly affected and five cars and a lorry crashed in a pile-up on the M1 near junction 25 at Sandiacre. 'Some people haven't got a clue how to drive in the snow,' said Inspector Bob Sheppard of the Nottingham Police Traffic Department. 'They're just going about like it was a sunny day. They are driving like idiots.' On the 23rd February, blizzards scoured Derbyshire and many rural roads were closed. Conditions in the East Midlands – the worst for three years – caused extensive traffic disruption and delayed flights at the regional airport.

With March came optimism for better weather, after what had seemed to many observers as the most protracted and dourest spell of weather for many years. Further rainstorms, cold temperatures and gales sent the Easter bunny diving for his hole. On the 15th February, high winds are thought to have blown a man to his death in the Grantham Canal at Bassingfield near Gamston, Nottinghamshire. The gales also caused problems in St Matthew's church, Nottingham where the congregation were celebrating Mother's Day. The roof came off 'like a sheet of paper' and landed on top of the vicarage. Mothers were not best pleased.

James McCarthy and Diamond passing Hope church in the winter of 1949. Mr McCarthy's Loose Hill farm, at 1,000 ft above sea level and with no electricity (notice the paraffin), relied upon sleigh transport for weeks on end. (B Anderson-Baker)

Postscript

People from this region have always known that the weather deteriorates with the arrival of weekends. It is an obvious fact of life, now confirmed by a scientist following a 14-year global study.

Adrian Gordon of the Flinders Institute for Atmospheric and Marine Sciences in Adelaide, Australia concludes that temperatures fall at weekends when the warming effects of fuel-burning factories and vehicles taper off. The fall in temperature is said to be especially noticeable in the northern hemisphere. But by how much? On average, by two hundredths of a degree Celsius says Mr Gordon!

Glossary of Common Weather Terms

Altitude: Height above sea level.

Anticyclone: An area of high pressure bringing fine weather.

Atmosphere: A gaseous envelope surrounding the earth.

Aurora borealis: The Northern Lights a spectacular heavenly phenomenon producing brilliant displays of colour, caused by the atmospheric disturbance of oxygen and nitrogen by electrons and protons radiating from the sun.

Ball lightning: A suspended sphere of radiating energy explained as an electrical dust cloud, a slow-burning admixture of air and carbon or an ionised mass of gas.

Barometer: An instrument for measuring atmospheric pressure.

Clouds: Condensed water vapour.

Drought: A prolonged absence of precipitation.

Fog: Clouds of condensing water vapour resulting from the interaction of warm and cold air.

Front: The boundary between two masses of air of differing densities or temperatures.

Frost: Frozen dew or water vapour.

Gale: Wind measured in velocity between 34 and 40 knots.

Glaze: Rain which freezes on contact with the ground.

Hail: A form of precipitation consisting of ice pellets of more than 1 cm (0.39 inches) in diameter.

Hurricane: Wind measured in velocity in excess of 64 knots.

Lightning: A flash of energy produced by an electrical discharge between clouds or between clouds and the ground.

Mist: An increase in water droplet concentrations in the air resulting in decreased visibility.

Rain: Liquid precipitation whose individual droplets measure up to 6 mm (0.24 inches in diameter).

Rainbow: Optical phenomena occuring when sunlight is refracted into spectral colours by shower clouds. The larger the raindrops, the more intense the rainbow.

Sleet: Form of precipitation consisting of a mixture of melting snow and rain.

Snow: Frozen flakes of ice in the shape of six-pointed stars.

Thermometer: Instrument for measuring temperature.

Thunder: The audible consequences of air particle compression and collision in air vacuums created by lightning activity.

Thunderstorm: Onset of rapidly rising moist air attended by heavy rain, thunder and lightning.

Tornado: A violent columnar spiral of wind travelling at great speed.

Wind: The process of pressure equalisation: air moving from high pressure to low pressure.

Acknowledgements

I would like to thank all those people of Derbyshire and Nottinghamshire, some no longer living in the counties, who replied to my requests via local newspapers, for pictorial memories of weather incidents from the past. Particular thanks go to: the vicar and Parochial Church Council of Youlgreave, Kirk Ireton Parochial Church Council and Nottingham Local Studies Library for its provision of many photographs from the Nottingham Evening Post.

L.M.

Index

128